The Student Lab Report Handbook

A Guide to Content, Style, and Formatting for Effective Science Lab Reports

Second Edition

John D. Mays

Austin, Texas
2014

We gratefully acknowledge Dr. Christina Swan for her contribution of the example lab report entitled, "Genetics of Organisms."

ISBN 978-0-9883228-7-5

Published by

Novare Science and Math
P. O. Box 92934
Austin, TX 78709-2934

888-720-9953
novarescienceandmath.com

Printed in the United States of America.

For information about the full catalog of texts and resources available from Novare Science and Math, visit the website at novarescienceandmath.com.

Contents

NOVARE
SCIENCE & MATH

Preface to the Teacher

Writing Lab Reports from Scratch

For decades it has been standard practice for students to document science experiments using programmed lab manuals. Typically, these lab manuals contain a number of fill-in-the-blank questions, and require the students to enter data in pre-printed charts or make graphs on pre-printed grids. Such programmed activities do little in the way of teaching students to think independently. Neither do such manuals contribute much to the development of the student's ability to explain the theory behind the phenomena, the experimental process itself, or the results that were obtained. Higher-level goals such as students' self-organization, integration of mathematical and historical concepts with scientific study, and skillful communication of scientific data and results are addressed only minimally, if at all.

No school or college should be satisfied with such a methodology. The paramount concern of enabling students to think for themselves in a scientific context requires must be supported by each phase of the experimental process. Writing reports challenges students to think through the issue at hand and develop the linguistic, mathematical, technical, and organizational skills to synthesize their responses to it. This handbook addresses the need for support documentation designed for such a learning environment.

In their ninth grade year, students should begin writing lab reports *from scratch*. The learning process should be distributed over the course of the year, with performance expectations gradually increased so that by the end of ninth grade, students know how to write a good report using proper scientific language and technical style, including proper use of tables, graphs, and figures for presentation and analysis of data and observations. Right from the beginning of this process, students should use computer tools to prepare their documentation. Training on the use of these tools should be integrated into the ninth grade curriculum. Further training on more sophisticated computer tools such as spreadsheets and statistical analysis applications should be rolled out in science courses as the need arises.

Students at all grade levels should be engaged in activities that focus on what many educators call the *tools of learning*. Beginning at the high school level and continuing through college, key curricular components in science classes should be oriented toward the development of these tools, including skills in planning, organization, observation, experimentation, analysis, and documentation. The process of preparing a lab report from scratch involves activities that correlate very closely with these curricular goals. For this reason, the regular development of detailed lab reports should be an integral part of the science classes in any high school or college.

This handbook describes standard requirements for content, style, and formatting for school lab reports, patterned after standard presentation models found in the scientific literature. Included also are details for using computer tools to create graphs, descriptions of common deficiencies found in student reports, and four complete sample reports representing different courses of study and different levels of sophistication. Students should study this handbook and seek to master the preparation of science lab reports as part of their experience in their science studies.

The Purpose of Laboratory Activities

Laboratory activities in science courses are often taken for granted, so it will be of value to pause for a moment and consider the purpose of labs even further. Laboratory experiments play an important role in the development of a student's knowledge, particularly in the development of the tools of learning.

Good work in science requires carefully developed ability to observe, to document with accuracy, to take measurements properly, and to communicate effectively. A significant part of scientific inquiry involves the development of experimental techniques which can isolate variables so that cause and effect relationships may be determined and analyzed. In the high-tech world of contemporary scientific research, constructing an effective experiment can be very difficult, and can only be accomplished by individuals who have been trained to handle sophisticated apparatus properly and to anticipate factors and side effects which may affect experimental results. Likewise, interpreting scientific data in contemporary research is often an exceedingly difficult task requiring great experience and skill. A solid science laboratory program at the high school level contributes to the student's acquisition of skills prerequisite to further successful scientific endeavors. But regardless of whether a student pursues a vocation in a scientific field, a student who successfully completes a good program in high school science will benefit tremendously by having his or her own analytical and communication skills sharpened, and by experiencing first hand the challenges of conducting a valid experiment.

Implementation: Recommendations for High School Teachers

As you teach your students how to write their lab reports from scratch, I offer the following advice:

1. Assign five or six lab reports during the year. This will give students adequate practice at report writing without burdening them too heavily. If you do more experiments than this during the year, have the students document some of them using a short form or summary report, and some of them with a full lab report as described in this *Handbook*.

2. When introducing ninth grade students to writing lab reports, assign students to begin reading the *Handbook* right at the beginning of the year, and follow up with their first report assignment just a couple of weeks later. The first report should include a data table but no graph. This way, students can read the early chapters in the *Handbook*, such as Chapters 1–4 and 8, and learn basic formatting during the first report or two. The second or third experiment can include a graph in the report, and at that time students can begin studying Chapters 5–7. Consider also offering graphing tutorials for PCs and Macs. Use a digital projector to go through the graph configuration procedure with the students. If they have laptop computers, have them bring them to the tutorial and configure their own graphs in parallel with the instruction. Such an introduction will help prevent students feeling daunted at the new tasks before them.

3. Require each student to write an individual report. Although practicing scientists do typically submit jointly written articles for publication, all students need to learn how to write good reports for themselves. High school science courses are not the place to let students off the hook by letting them depend on one team member who happens to be good at it.

4. Scale your grading standards to the students' progress through your program. There is a lot that goes into writing a good report, so on the first try, grading should focus on the basics of structure, formatting, and content. On the second and third reports and beyond, students should be expected continually to improve their submissions so that by the end of their ninth grade year their reports are solid in every detail. By midway through their tenth grade year, their skill at data analysis and report writing should be very well developed.

5. Encourage your students to submit drafts of their reports for review well in advance of the final report due date. If this draft submission is optional rather than required, students will appreciate it as an opportunity. Without spending a great deal of time grading the report in detail, you will be able to identify numerous elements of the report that need to be corrected or improved. Regardless of whether the students really want to learn, or whether they just want a decent grade in the course, this drafting process will help.

6. The first couple of times you do lab activities that require graphs, consider requiring your students to prepare the graph in Excel or Pages in advance of the report due date and submit it for approval, prior to incorporating it into the report itself. Getting the graphs right is a key way to improve the quality of a report. Conversely, getting the graphs wrong is a key way to ruin an otherwise decent report. Again, your students will all benefit from this pre-submittal review process.

Results You Can Expect

For many years, I have witnessed an event that occurs annually somewhere around Thanksgiving. Students who graduated from high school the previous spring come home from college and drop in for a visit. They tell of the science lab course they are in and the praise they received from their TA on the occasion of the first lab report. Invariably, the TA says something like, "Where did you learn how to write a lab report like this? No one ever knows how to do this when they are first starting college." After the student responds that he or she learned how to write lab reports in high school, the TA usually says, "I am impressed! Where did you go to high school?" By using this manual in high school science classes to teach your students how to write their lab reports, your students can be prepared for college this way and will be ahead of their peers in their lab courses.

New in the Second Edition

Teachers who are already familiar with this *Handbook* should take note that some of the changes and additions in this second edition are significant. These include:

1. I now recommend that students be required to use indelible ink when making entries in their lab journals. See Section 1.2.

2. Chapter 3 on Writing Style has been expanded and revised quite a bit. In particular, the verb issues associated with tense, voice, and mood are explained in a lot more detail.

3. I have replaced the term *experimental error* with the more appropriate term *percent difference*. See Section 4.7. Since January of 2013 I have used this terminology in my texts as well.

4. The computer instructions for preparing graphs in Chapter 7 now include both PCs and Macs. The instructions include adding trendlines and uncertainty bars in both cases. Instructions for new (current) software versions appear in the chapter first. Older versions are still included in later sections.

Preface to the Student

Introductory Advice

In today's technical world, learning how to write a quality lab report from scratch is important for virtually every student. Writing lab reports well is not that hard, it just takes guidance (this book) and practice. And though it sounds nerdy to say this, writing good reports can be fun and rewarding, especially as you begin to take pride in your own abilities and in work well done. But as you begin learning how to write lab reports from scratch, here are two pieces of advice to keep in mind.

1. Never wait until the night before a report is due to begin writing it. You know this already, and you know that a well-written report requires thought, planning, proofreading, and careful editing. What you may not know yet is that when you are preparing a science lab report, you may find errors in your calculations or graphs that you are not sure how to correct. If you want to submit a quality report, it is important that you make these discoveries with plenty of time to spare so that you can get the advice you need and make the corrections.

2. Never email any tables or text to other teammates, and never ask for anyone to email such to you. You have lived in the digital era all of your life and are accustomed to sending things to your friends via various digital media. But hopefully you have already been taught that you must write your own material when submitting any paper or report, whether for a grade or for publication. Quotations come only from authorities (not your lab partner) and must be properly cited. Naturally, you will discuss your data, results, and conclusions with other students in your team. But to make absolutely sure that you never cross over the line into plagiarism, even unintentionally, never send report content to or receive report content from anyone. Write your own report, using your own words, your own tables, and your own graphs.

Learning Objectives for a Secondary Science Lab Program

I believe that students should know the learning objectives associated with the academic work they are doing. There are quite a few important skills that can only be developed in a laboratory environment, which is why experiments are part of nearly every science course. The learning objectives for science lab classes at any high-quality educational institution will be similar and will include those listed below:

After successfully completing the required sequence of science courses at your school or college, you will be able to do the following:

1. State and follow standard laboratory safety practices.

2. Correctly identify and use standard laboratory apparatus.

3. Use proper care in setting up apparatus to protect equipment and minimize percent difference between prediction and result.

4. Describe and follow the proper methods for making measurements with common instruments. This includes identifying the types of errors that can introduce inaccuracies in measurements and describing how to avoid them.

5. State the role of precision in taking measurements, and relate this to the significant digits in a measurement.
6. Apply sound scientific methods to conducting experiments and to writing reports.
7. Maintain a proper lab journal.
8. Clearly explain the theoretical background behind an experiment, using quantitative analysis where appropriate.
9. Use quantitative predictions from scientific theory to form testable hypotheses.
10. Clearly and efficiently describe a scientific procedure and the results and discoveries that followed.
11. Use appropriate care in experimental procedures and data collection.
12. Present calculations and data in a clear, organized fashion such that others can verify calculations or check results. This includes development of tables and graphs using standard scientific units and formatting.
13. Apply quantitative error analysis to experimental data as appropriate.
14. Apply qualitative analysis to experimental results as appropriate.
15. Estimate uncertainty in measurements.
16. Apply cogent reasoning to analysis and discussion of experimental results. This includes reasonable identification of the factors that contributed to the percent difference between predictions and experimental results.
17. Use computer tools to take data, graph data, and develop reports.
18. Use clear, concise, and accurate language in a technical style in scientific reports.
19. Cooperate with team members successfully to accomplish each of the above objectives.

Chapter 1
Using a Lab Journal

1.1 Why Lab Journals Are Important

Scientists engaged in experimental research keep detailed journals documenting every aspect of their work. Because of the importance of journaling in the scientific community, and because of the close connection between journaling of scientific experiments and the need for science students to develop excellence in written expression, each student in a laboratory science course must maintain a thorough lab journal.

The lab report is the final product documenting a laboratory exercise and is submitted to the instructor for grading. During the experiment itself, you must individually record your activities, observations, and the data acquired by you and your team in your lab journal. All of the information from the experiment that you will need later to write the lab report should be written in the journal at the time of the experiment. Later, as you are preparing your report, the lab journal is your source for all of the information that you will present. You should never rely on memory alone or on notes kept by other team members to document your work. Your instructor may require you to submit your lab journal with the report for grading, or it may be checked and graded separately.

Figure 1-1. The Mead 09127 composition book.

Good choices for lab journal use are the National 53-108 hard cover, or the Mead 09127 flexible composition book shown in Figure 1-1. Both of these contain quadrille (graph paper) pages, which facilitate the tabulation of your experimental data and the construction of any graphs or diagrams you may need to draw during the laboratory exercise. Any similar composition book with quadrille pages will suffice. Do not use a spiral-bound notebook, a three-ring binder, or any notebook with ruled paper.

1.2 Pencil or Pen?

In the first edition of this book, I strongly encouraged students to use only pencil when writing in their lab journals. This is because I encourage students to use pencil for everything else in their science and math classes. However, I learned something new since that edition was published—practicing scientists now use only indelible (that is, non-erasable) ink in their lab journals. As described above, lab journals are the primary record of experimental work. Sometimes a scientist's lab journals become key evidence in cases of establishing priority in a discovery or in identifying crucial details that could affect the outcome of a patent-infringement lawsuit. When documents are of such importance, it is of paramount importance that they are written in indelible ink. For this reason, I now encourage students to use only blue or black ink in their lab journals and pencil for their other work in science and math. (Colors other than blue or black are not acceptable.) Ultimately, your teacher will decide whether you are required to maintain your lab journal in ink or if pencil is acceptable. But my view now is that as a student, you should develop the habits of a real scientist. This means maintaining your lab journal in ink.

Maintaining lab journals in ink obviously introduces a bit of a problem. Your journal is to be neat and free of smudges, doodling, stray marks, and so on. So what do you do if you discover that you made an error? For example, what if an entire table of data is full of wrong entries? You do exactly what a practicing scientist would do—you *carefully* circle the incorrect information (in ink), and *neatly* cross through it with one line. You should make sure what you cross out remains legible. Make a note as to why it is to be ignored, and put the date and your initials on the note. This way, it is evident to everyone that you knew at the time that there were errors and you made note of them. You want to avoid the possibility of someone thinking that the data were changed later, after the fact.

Now, you may be thinking that all this formal lab journal stuff is goofy. You may think that you are just a student taking a science class and have no intention of become a practicing scientist, so there won't be any patent-infringement lawsuits over your lab work. Well, you never know where you will end up. Plenty of people change their majors halfway through college. So every student needs to learn proper scientific laboratory methods. And the right time to begin learning those methods is *right now*. This applies whether you are in junior high, high school, or college.

1.3 General Lab Journal Principles

The following principles apply to everything you write in your lab journal.

1. Every time you make an entry in your journal, the entry should be dated and well-organized. As suggested by Figure 1-2, it is imperative that lab journals are kept neat, clean, and free of extraneous marks or doodling.
2. When you write the date, make the date unambiguous by spelling out the month, as in the dates 6 February, 2014 or February 6, 2014.[1]
3. Begin a new page in your journal for each experiment.

Figure 1-2. Keep your lab journal exquisitely neat.

4. Do not leave blank pages or space in your lab journal. If there is blank space remaining at the end of an experiment, *neatly* cross through it. This way no one can go back and add in information that wasn't part of the work at the time.
5. If you have printouts, photographs, or other loose items, tape them into your journal and sign and date the entry.
6. Your journal should contain only information and data from work where you were present and personally involved. If you need information from a teammate pertaining to a day when you were not present, enter the information and make a note of where the information came from and when you transcribed it into your journal.
7. Put your name and contact information on the front of your lab journal.

1 This is because Europeans write the date before the month in dates, whereas Americans write the month first. To an American, 2/6/14 means February 6. To a European, it means June 2.

1.3 What to Write In Your Lab Journal

Examples of the kind of information that you should enter in your journal are listed below.

1. Date of entry.

   Every entry must be dated so you can retrace what happened if something turns out wrong or if you later find that you have conflicting information. As mentioned above, make the date unambiguous by spelling out the month. Include the time of day only if it happens to be relevant to the experiment.

2. Names of other people working in the team.

   List the first and last name of everyone who worked on your team that day. List the names separately for each day you work so that you know exactly who was present and when.

3. The purpose or goal of your experiment.

4. Your experimental hypothesis.

5. Lists and quantities of all equipment, materials, and supplies used.

   Be sure to include the makes and model numbers of all electronic equipment or major apparatus. This may not seem necessary for a school science class, but it is standard practice among scientists and you need to get in the habit. When different teams of scientists compare experimental results, an important factor will be to see if any differences in experimental results are attributable to differences in the mechanical or electronic equipment. Now is the time to develop good habits for documenting the equipment used.

6. Tables documenting all data taken during the experiment.

   As you record data, it is crucial that you record the units of measure as well. Always record the units of measure in the same units as displayed by the measurement device. If you need to convert your data into different units, then it is a good idea to make another column in your journal for the new values converted to different units. (Also record the unit conversion factors or equations you use). In your report, you should show both the original units in which the data were collected and the converted values you need for the calculations you must perform.

   You must also record all data using the correct number of significant digits for the measurement instrument you used. If you measure out 8 mL of liquid, you need to record this value as 8.0 mL, 8.00 mL, 8.000 mL, etc., depending on the precision of your measurement instrument. Do not simply write 8 mL unless your measurement actually was made with only one significant digit (which won't happen).

7. Detailed records of all qualitative observations.

   Experimental observations are often chiefly documented by data. But any nontrivial qualitative observation you make that relates to the experiment needs to be documented as well. This is true in any science course, but it is especially common in biology and chemistry. Qualitative observations you may need to document involve color, appearance, texture, odor, action (such as what happened or did not happen in certain circumstances), taste, or other observations.

8. Descriptions of steps or procedures followed, problems encountered, solutions implemented.

   Write down exactly what you and your team do. All standard procedures should be documented. If you encounter a problem, you should document it. If you have to do some work over again because of an error or an unexpected experimental result, you should document it and explain what happened. If you think of a good way to work around some unexpected problem, you should document that, too. (Your teacher will appreciate that.)

9. Preliminary calculations, or calculations needed during the procedure.

   Sometimes you will need to use data collected in an early part of a procedure to perform calculations prior to continuing with the experiment. These calculations should all be documented in your lab journal. Your lab journal is also the proper place to document the calculations you make after all the data have been collected. These final calculations can then be typed into appropriate tables in your lab report.

10. Diagrams of apparatus and experimental setup.

    If your experimental setup was simple enough that it can be explained in a few sentences, a diagram is probably not necessary. If the setup is complex and cannot be clearly described in a paragraph or two, then a diagram or photograph of the setup is needed. If you take photos, be sure to document whose camera, phone, or computer the photos are on so that you can find them later.

11. Preliminary graphs which may be needed during the experiment to assess progress.

    If you need to make a preliminary graph of your data to get an idea of how the experiment is progressing, the lab journal is the proper place to do it—not on a piece of scrap paper.

12. Names, phone numbers, and reference information.

    If you have to contact anyone outside your immediate experimental team, such as a supplier or scientific expert, then that person's contact information, as well as the information you obtained from that person, should all be documented in your lab journal. Think of it this way: In a real working research lab one frequently needs to consult with a manufacturer's representative or an experienced person at another lab. Whatever information is obtained needs to be documented for the benefit of those who continue to work in the lab after you are gone. In our journals we need to make it easy for those working after us to retrace our steps, to follow up with new questions that may need to be posed to previously contacted experts, and so on. This kind of information can be critical and can save future researchers a lot of time. So, as mentioned above, now is the time to develop good habits. If you have to contact anyone about your work on a particular project or experiment, document the contact thoroughly. Write down how to reach them, what they told you, notes about any materials they commit to send to you, and so on.

13. Locations and/or sources of printed reference materials.

    Any reference materials used during the lab, or which come to your attention during the lab and may be needed later, should be documented. This is both to have the reference information you used during the experiment, as well as to remind yourself of resources you might need that you may forget about later.

Chapter 2
Formatting and Printing Requirements

2.1 The Importance of Proper Formatting

The way your report looks is extremely important. In scientific work, there are common practices that govern everything about the way scientists document their work. If you write a scientific paper that is to be published, the formatting requirements for that article will be extensive, detailed, and rigorously enforced. For these reasons, part of your laboratory experience in your present laboratory course is to produce lab reports that meet a very specific set of formatting and content requirements.

These requirements were not just invented to make your life hard. The requirements specified here are designed to teach you how formal scientific papers are formatted. If you intend to enter into a branch of scientific study, writing reports according to the specifications described here will help you prepare for that work. But even if you don't intend to be a scientist, there is still great value in mastering the report requirements in this book. Most students have to take a laboratory science course in college, and if you already know how to prepare a proper lab report, you will reap the benefit. Further, in just about every professional field, people have to write reports. Learning the basics of scientific reporting will make it much easier in the future for you to learn how to write reports in your other classes or for other kinds of work.

2.2 Formatting Requirements for Lab Reports

Your printed report must meet the following requirements:

1. Margins and line spacing.

   Reports must be typed with single-spaced text and printed on white paper using one-inch margins.

2. Fonts.

   Use a plain font such as Times New Roman. The point size for the text should be 12 pt. When setting up graphs in a program such as Excel or Pages, it is common for the default fonts in axis labels, axis scales, and so on to be a sans serif font such as Arial. It is permissible for these kinds of labels in graphs or other figures to be either Times New Roman or Arial.

3. Labels and titles on tables, graphs, and figures.

   Formatting requirements for the labels and titles on tables, graphs, and figures are discussed in Section 3.4.

4. Reference citations.

   Formatting requirements for citations in the References section of the report are discussed in Section 5.9.

5. Colors.

   Do not use color for your report text; the text of your report must be entirely in black and white. You may print your report either in color or black and white, unless you have photographs or other figures that require color for them to be read properly. However, note that graphing software in Microsoft and Apple products automatically uses different colors for multiple curves displayed on the same graph. If you will be printing in black and white, these colors will not be distinguishable. To make the correspondence between the legend and the graph work in black and white, the symbols used for the data points on the two curves must be different. In some applications the default symbol shapes for all data are the same, and the graph depends on color to distinguish the curves from each other in the legend. For black and white prints, you will need to determine how to change the symbol shapes for each data set (each separate curve) and make the symbols on each curve different from the symbols on the other curves.

6. Extra graphics.

   Reports should look clean, neat, and plain, with crisp formatting. Do not attempt to dress up the appearance with fancy graphics, title pages, colors, and so on. Plain is good.

7. Stapling.

   Do not enclose the report in a binder or plastic cover, and do not use a cover sheet. Simply staple the pages together in the upper left hand corner.

8. Technology problems.

   Do not submit a report that contains errors due to your software or printing technology. You are expected to proofread your report and identify and correct any errors in your printed report that are due to computer or printer problems. For example, it has happened when copying a graph from a spreadsheet to a word processor that only half the graph appears after it is pasted in. Low-resolution graphics and equations may be seriously fuzzy or even illegible, depending on your software and your printer. Sometimes your printer cartridge runs out of toner in the middle of a page and the page fades out toward the bottom. You should not turn in a report containing these kinds of errors.

2.3 Planning Ahead

After spending a lot of time and effort putting together a high-quality lab report, the last thing you want is to find out at 1:45 a.m. that you are out of printer paper, or your printer is out of toner, or some other disaster. You should always plan your work so that if you have technical difficulties you will have time to get them resolved prior to the report due date. In general, you should prepare your report far enough in advance so that you have time to proofread, make corrections, find a different printer, get help with graphs, and so on, rather than waiting until the night before the report is due.

Chapter 3
Writing Style

As I discuss writing style in this chapter, I will frequently need to refer to the different sections in a lab report. In Chapters 4 and 5, we will address in detail the content of the lab report, what the different sections in the report are for, and what to write about in each of them. But for you to follow the discussion in the present chapter, you need to know at least what these report sections are called and where they occur. Accordingly, here is the list:

Heading
Abstract (upper-level courses only)
Purpose
Background
Experimental Procedure
Results
Discussion
Conclusion
References

3.1 Technical Writing Is Different

Lab reports belong to the literary genre known as *technical writing*. Style for technical writing is very different from styles used in other types of English composition. The purpose of technical style is to be as clear and unambiguous as possible. Not all forms of writing strive for these qualities. For example, if you are writing a piece of fiction, you might make a certain passage deliberately ambiguous or unclear just to build suspense or create a sense of confusion. Technical writing is never like this. Instead, technical writing is deliberately plain and free of ornamentation, figures of speech, strange vocabulary (except appropriate technical vocabulary, of course), and rhetorical flourishes.

Technical writing is often described as *dry*. When writing technical materials, your writing should be deliberately plain because, again, the purpose is to communicate scientific information as clearly and unambiguously as possible.

When you engage in creative writing, you use a creative vocabulary to add spice and variety to your prose. You also use metaphors, similes, and many other figures of speech to create texture and beauty. Your goal in creative writing is to make your work as fascinating as possible, to create a certain tone and mood, and to give your reader a pleasurable reading experience.

These are not the goals of technical writing. Creative vocabulary and figures of speech interfere with the scientific objective of clarity of meaning. In creative writing, students are taught to avoid repeating the same terms. Instead, students are encouraged to use a great variety of adverbs and adjectives to add color and interest to your work. By contrast, technical writers *deliberately* use the same adjectives and adverbs repeatedly without variety so the reader knows the author means to say the same thing each time. Different adjectives should be used only when you intend to make a deliberate distinction.

3.2 Concision (or, to be a bit less concise: Conciseness)

One of the goals of technical writing is to say thoroughly what you need to say, but to say it using no more words than are necessary. In other words, you need to be *concise*. Any phrase or sentence that does not add specific, important content to your paper should be eliminated. Always ask yourself if words can be eliminated while preserving accuracy and thoroughness, and if so, eliminate them.

Now, being concise does not mean leaving out important information. Your reports must be both *thorough* and *concise*. As with any difficult task worth doing, learning to write this way takes time and practice. It also takes conscientious editing and proofreading. A sentence you write today can appear completely useless later when you are proofreading. Thinking back to what I wrote at the end of the previous chapter, this is another reason why you should not try to prepare your reports the night before they are due. Good students prepare their papers in advance of the due date so they can set them aside for a day or two and then proofread them again. This is an excellent way to improve the quality of your writing.

Here are some examples of wordy phrases that can be edited to make them more concise:

Very Wordy:

> "What can be concluded from this experiment and observation is that friction in simple machines does affect...."

Concise:

> "In conclusion, friction in simple machines does affect...."

Wordy:

> "The efficiency was seen to be simply the result of...."

Concise:

> "The efficiency is the result of...."

3.3 Avoiding Slang

Slang

In a technical document such as a lab report, slang should be completely avoided. It is very challenging for students to learn how to write formally because slang is such an integral part of the way we speak these days. To help give you the right frame of mind for writing a lab report, here is a suggestion: write as if you were writing a letter to a corporate CEO that you have never met to ask for a job. In other words, think about being *formal, professional,* and *dignified* (without adding any flowery or unnecessary language). Leave out all cuteness and personal feeling. Be as staid and professional as you can.

To illustrate further, here are some example phrases to avoid:

- Slang and informal speech, such as "We just shoved the thing across the table and it worked," or "The ingredients were then dumped into a beaker."
- Conversational words and phrases such as *anyway, so, well, now,* and the like.
- Statements of personal feeling such as "This lab was really fun!" or "Our results were awesome."

I need to warn you against trying to write the way I, the author, am writing to you in this book. When I write textbooks for students, I do use words like *well* and *now*. I also use the first person pronouns

I and *we*, and the second person pronoun *you*. These are stylistic choices I make in order that the book will be more accessible and more interesting for you to read. But that is *not* how I write when I write a technical report. Different types of writing require different styles for the documents to be effective. One of the things I do to make my textbooks appealing is use personal pronouns. But when we write technical reports, we avoid personal pronouns because our goal is to write plainly and formally. You might say that your paper is *supposed* to be lifeless and boring!

Pronouns

Returning to the use of pronouns, it is acceptable to use the personal pronoun *we* after you have made it clear that you are referring to your team. Other personal pronouns such as *I* and *you* should be avoided. For actions performed by people other than your group, refer to them impersonally and formally, as in "The instructor provided us with a beaker of an unknown substance." When describing actions performed by the team, do not refer to individual team members' names. Refer instead only to actions performed by *the team*, *the group*, or *a team member*.

You may feel that technical writing style as I have described it seems boring. However, there is one way in which it is not boring: if you are reporting an *unexpected* result from an experiment, then any scientist reading that paper will get excited about it. This is what gets scientists excited—high quality experiments that produce unexpected results. When the unexpected occurs, we all learn something and science itself might even take a leap forward. If the results of your experiment are unexpected, then the place to say so is in the Discussion and Conclusion sections of your report. (We will discuss these in the next two chapters.) However, just make sure you continue to write in a dignified, formal way, even when you write something like, "Our experimental results were completely unexpected, and were not at all in line with our hypothesis." Examples of this style are included in the example lab reports in Chapter 9.

3.4 Referring to Tables, Graphs, and Figures

Other than text, there are three common elements that occur regularly in lab reports—tables, graphs (sometimes also referred to as charts or plots), and figures. In a technical report, there are specific conventions for referring to these that you need to follow. As you read through these conventions (rules) and the examples, also look at the figures that appear later in this manual and in the example reports in Chapter 9. You will see that the rules described here are followed in each case.

A *table* displays data or the results of computations based on data. A *graph* has one or two (or even three) axes and displays data associated with variables or relations between variables. A *figure* is either photograph, a diagram, or some other kind of graphic. The first cardinal rule about placing these elements in your report is this:

> Rule 1 *No table, graph, or figure may appear in your report unless you refer to it in the text.*

You must have a sentence in the text directing the reader's attention to the table, graph, or figure the reader needs to refer to. Usually, this referring sentence is a simple statement such as "Experimental data are presented in Tables 1 and 2." Then you place the two tables you just mentioned in the report soon after that remark. The reference should come first and the element you are referring to should come soon after your reference. Your reference and the referenced element should be placed on the same page if possible. If that is not possible because your reference occurs near the bottom of the page, place the element referred to at the top of the next page.

The second cardinal rule is this:

Rule 2 *Every table, graph, and figure must have both a label and a title.*

Labels are designations such as "Table 4," "Graph 1," or "Figure 3." After the label comes the title, which is a brief but specific description of the content of the table, graph, or figure. Your title may not be a vague or non-descriptive phrase such as "Graph" or "Our diagram." The title needs to identify the contents more specifically. Consider these examples:

Label	Title
Table 1.	Mass and volume data for copper.
Table 3.	Residue mass data from vacuum filtration with a Büchner funnel.
Graph 1.	Velocity vs. time for experimental setup B.
Graph 2.	Comparison of predicted and experimental accelerations.
Figure 1.	Experimental setup for measurement of the speed of light.
Figure 4.	Severe exfoliation after four days.

Notice that each of the example titles describes the content of the table, graph, or figure. Second, notice that titles should not include personal pronouns such as "our." Instead of a title like "Our setup," you should write "Experimental setup." Third, avoid awkward or vague titles such as "Graph we used to guide the lab."

The examples above adhere to two specific rules about the punctuation of labels and titles. This brings up the third cardinal rule, which is this:

Rule 3 *Labels and titles for tables, graphs, and figures must strictly adhere to technical conventions for punctuation.*

There are two punctuation rules: (1) Capitalize the label and the first word only in the title, unless proper names appear. In the examples above, the first letters of each label and each title are capitalized. The only other capital letters are in the proper names that appear in the titles of Table 3 and Graph 1. In the Graph 1 title, the letter B functions as a proper name. (2) Place a period after the label and another period after the title.

There is one final rule for referring to tables, graphs, and figures which is:

Rule 4 *The label and title go together either immediately above or immediately below the element being referenced.*

You can see examples of such placement in the figures later in this manual and in the example lab reports in Chapter 9. Do not allow a page break to separate the label and title from the element they refer to. If your software separates them, you must force them to stay together. There are a couple of ways to address this. The sophisticated way is by the use of paragraph styles with appropriate settings. The quick and unsophisticated way is to insert a page break right before the label and title to force them to the next page with the element they are associated with.

3.5 Tips for Vocabulary

From what you have read so far in this chapter, you probably already know that when writing a lab report you need to pay close attention the words you use—your vocabulary. You already know, for example, to avoid slang terms such as wacko, awesome, crazy, and the like. Here are a few additional tips about vocabulary.

- As consistently as possible, use formal or scientific verbs such as *observe*, *measure*, *verify*, *record*, *rinse*, *assemble*, *ignite*, *retain*, *transfer*, *discard*, and *specify*. Stay away from the thesaurus—fancy variations to standard scientific terms are out of place in a technical paper.

- When referring to the experiment you are working on, use the term *experiment*. Do not refer to it as "this lab" or "the lab." You are not working *on* a lab; you worked *in* a lab on an *experiment*. Now, it is true that *everyone* refers to the report you write after an experiment as a *lab report*, hence the name of this book. Regardless, it will be good if you can train yourself to refer to the experimental work as the *experiment* instead of the *lab*. Refer to the room where the experiment took place as *the lab*.

- When referring to equipment and materials, do not capitalize the names of items unless they contain a proper name, such as in Bunsen burner, Büchner funnel, and Erlenmeyer flask. This goes for your equipment list as well. When you list out the equipment used in the experiment, don't capitalize anything except proper names.

- When referring to equations, avoid the word *formula*, which is roughly synonymous with the term *recipe*, unless you mean to use it this way. In most cases, you should use the more accurate terms *equation*, *law*, or *relation*. One correct place to use the term *formula* is when referring to a chemical formula such as the molecular formula of a compound.

- The word *data* is a plural noun straight from Latin, and it should be used with plural verbs, as in "The data *are* shown in Table 1." If you need to refer to a single data value, use *datum* (the Latin singular, also used in English), *data point*, or *data value*. I usually use the term *data value*, but if you want to impress people with your Latin, feel free to write *datum*.

- Avoid the error, very common these days, of saying *based off*... Nothing is ever *based off* anything else. Things are *based on* other things, as in "Our prediction was *based on* the solubility rules published in the text."

3.6 Guidelines for Tense, Voice, and Mood

A complete lesson in English grammar would take a small book. We are not going to get into that much detail here. However, there are a few important grammatical do's and don'ts that require a small amount of English grammar to understand. For the benefit of those who aren't experts in English grammar (and few of us are), I will explain the grammar as concisely as possible in the following three subsections. At the end of each subsection, I will summarize the do's and don't's. We must address three separate grammatical issues: tense, voice, and mood.

Verb Tense

When we include auxiliary words such as *has*, *have*, and *would have*, there are a lot of verb tenses in English—something like 30. But there are only a few verb tenses you need to know about and use in lab reports. The main tenses to use are the *simple present* and the *simple past*. There are occasions to use others tenses, and you will see some in the example reports in Chapter 9. But here we will focus on the main two. Here are examples illustrating these tenses:

simple present "Newton's Second Law of Motion, $F = ma$, implies that force and acceleration are directly proportional to each other."

"Using the values for mass and height shown above, the equation for gravitational potential energy gives a value of 255 J for the initial potential energy."

"The law of conservation of mass in chemical reactions states that mass is neither gained nor lost in chemical reactions."

simple past — "We began our analysis by calculating the percent difference for each mass."

"Since our solution failed to solidify as expected, our team repeated step two in the procedure."

"Our team found that only one of the four flames was blue."

In addition to these, you will need to use various forms of the verb *to be*. Examples of this are:

"We found plastic cups to be incompatible with this solution."

"Mass is neither gained nor lost in chemical reactions."

"Nitrile gloves are not appropriate for work involving nitric acid."

"Our team found that only one of the four flames was blue. The rest were various shades of red."

The examples above illustrate when to use to present and past tenses. Throughout your report, use the present tense when referring to scientific principles that were known before you did the experiment and are still correct after the experiment. Use the past tense to refer to events that occurred before and during your experiment.

Don't use the future tense at all. It is artificial to write in the future tense when everyone who is reading your report knows that the experiment has already been performed. The one exception to this rule might occur in the report's conclusion. For example, if you have occasion to discuss future experimental work, you may write a statement such as "In the second part of the experiment our team will attempt to validate these initial results."

In summary:

- Use the present tense when referring to scientific principles that were known before you did the experiment and are still correct after the experiment.
- Use the past tense to refer to events that occurred before and during your experiment.
- Don't use the future tense at all, except possibly in your Conclusion.

Voice

There are two voices in English, the *active voice* and the *passive voice*. Your entire report, except for the Experimental Procedure section, should be written in the active voice. In general, the Experimental Procedure section may be written either in the active voice or the passive voice, but many instructors require the Experimental Procedure to be written in the passive voice.

In a sentence written in the active voice, you first name the subject and you follow the subject with the verb that says what the subject is doing. This voice has the effect of emphasizing the subject of the sentence. Here are example sentences written in the active voice:

"Our team conducted seven separate trials." (subject: our team)

"The solution immediately changed color." (subject: the solution)

"One team member measured the volume of the solution in a graduated cylinder."
(subject: one team member)

In a sentence written in the passive voice, the object is mentioned first, the subject is usually not named (although it could be), and the verbs require helping verbs from the *to be* verb. Here are some examples using the simple past tense:

"The 16 solutions were prepared."	(unmentioned subject: the team)
"The powder was left to dry overnight."	(unmentioned subject: the team)
"The data collection was repeated."	(unmentioned subject: the person collecting the data)

If you look back at the two examples in Section 3.2, you will see that in both cases, the wordy phrase is in the passive voice. Converting the phrase into the active voice helps trim the phrase a lot. Instead of saying "what can be concluded is that friction affects so and so," you can simply say "friction affects so and so." In this case, the phrase in the passive voice can be eliminated entirely.

Except for the Experimental Procedure section, use the active voice throughout your report. Writing the Experimental Procedure section entirely in the active voice can sometimes be awkward. Recurrent use of phrases like "the team did this" and "the team did that" is unavoidable. For this reason, it is acceptable to use passive voice when describing the experimental procedure, and some instructors even require it. Writing in the passive voice results in phrases such as "the solution was heated" and "the apparatus was cleaned and the procedure was repeated." Since the unmentioned subject is always your team, there is no lack of clarity in writing this way in this particular case.

If you are going to write the procedure in the passive voice, then make it clear initially who performed various actions. So after mentioning your team a few times, it is acceptable to use a sentence such as "The remaining containers were filled using the same procedure."

In summary:

- Except for the Experimental Procedure Section, use the active voice throughout your report.
- In the Experimental Procedure section, you may write in the passive voice, or you may write in the active voice by referring to "our team" or "the team."

Mood

There are three moods in English, the *indicative*, the *imperative*, and the *subjunctive*. The three moods entail different verb forms. You will use the indicative mood nearly all of the time. The subjunctive may come up in your Discussion or Conclusion sections. The imperative should be avoided entirely. In fact, the main reason for even bringing up the topic of mood is to show you what the imperative mood is so that you can avoid it.

In the indicative mood, sentences make statements or ask questions. All of the examples we have looked at so far in this chapter are in the indicative mood. The previous eight sentences are all in the indicative mood.

In the imperative mood, sentences take the form of commands, as in these examples:

"Pour the solution into the graduated cylinder."

"Measure out 150 grams of potassium chloride."

"Avoid writing your Procedure section in the imperative mood."

A common mistake is for students to write the Experimental Procedure in the imperative mood, which has the effect of making the procedure read like a recipe: "Measure some of this, mix in some of that, bake at 450°F for 30 minutes." Often, students write their Experimental Procedure as a sequence of numbered steps, each one written in the imperative mood. However, writing in the imperative mood is poor form and you should avoid writing this way. Instead, write the Experimental Procedure in the indicative mood in the past tense, either in the active voice or passive voice, as described above.

To round out this discussion, I will at least mention the subjunctive mood briefly to show how it can arise in the context of a lab report. The subjunctive mood is used to express a wish, a suggestion, or a statement that is contrary to fact. My favorite example of a statement that is contrary to fact is the classic children's song "If I were a dinosaur..." We know a statement that begins this way is contrary to fact because no one is a dinosaur. Here are examples of scientific statements written in the subjunctive mood:

"If this experiment were performed at a higher temperature, the reaction would take place more rapidly."

"It is essential that distilled water be used to avoid contamination."

"We recommend that the two solutions be prepared simultaneously by different team members."

As you can see, statements of this kind are mostly likely to arise in the Conclusion of the report, where you are summarizing your results and commenting on ways to make the experiment more successful in the future. The second of these example statements might sound like something you would write in your Experimental Procedure, but it is not. In the procedure, you should not write as if you were talking to the reader, which could entail using the subjunctive. The only section in the report where it is appropriate to write this way is the Conclusion.

In summary:

- Do not write your Experimental Procedure in the imperative mood.
- The subjunctive mood is permissible in the Conclusion.

Chapter 4
Report Content Overview

This chapter contains a general outline that you can use to design a good report. In the following two chapters (5 and 6), you will find more detailed discussion of the contents for each section in the report.

4.1 Assumed Audience

As you put together your section content and decide what to say, assume that your reader is an intelligent person who is mathematically competent and who has a working scientific vocabulary, but do not assume that the reader was present at the experiment or has any idea of what the experiment was about. In other words, imagine that you are explaining your experiment to a teacher in another department or to a working professional. If it would be silly to explain something to such an individual (such as what length or volume are), then the explanation is probably out of place in your report. If an explanation of something seems necessary so that the individual would know what you are talking about, then that explanation probably does belong in your report.

4.2 Heading

The heading at the top of your report should include a title for the experiment, your name, the names of the other members of your experimental team, the date the experiment was performed, the date the report was submitted, the instructor's name, and the name of the class.

4.3 Abstract

Your instructor will tell you if an abstract is required. Abstracts are usually required in upper-level or advanced courses. The abstract is a very brief or even terse summary of the goal of the experiment, what was done, and what the results were.

4.4 Purpose

Here you state the purpose of the experiment in one or two sentences. Laboratory experiments are of two general types—those designed to test a hypothesis and those designed around students' exploration and discovery. These two general types of experiments have different purposes. Experiments in physics, and often in chemistry, are hypothesis-driven. In a hypothesis-driven experiment, one seeks to measure an experimental result (often the value of one or more particular variables) and compare it to the value predicted from the theory. In this case, the purpose statement should be about experimentally determining the value of a variable and comparing this experimental result to the values predicted from the equations in the theory. Here is an example purpose statement for this type of experiment:

> "The purpose of this experiment was to measure the rate of heat transfer out of a blackbody at certain conditions and compare experimental data to rate predictions based on the Stefan-Boltzmann law."

On the other hand, experiments in biology, earth science, astronomy, and sometimes chemistry are often discovery-driven, and are oriented around exploration and discovery rather than making specific predictions. In these experiments, the purpose statement should be about the goal of the exploratory process. State this goal as specifically as possible. Here is an example purpose statement for this type of experiment:

"The purpose of this experiment was to identify eight constellations and document their positions on the celestial sphere."

4.5 Background

The goal of the Background section is to inform your reader about the experiment so that your reader will have a clear idea of what you did, why you did it, and what your results mean. This section should include the elements below in the order listed. For high school science reports, this section of the report will require from one to four paragraphs (maybe more), depending on how complex the theory and the experiment are. In college lab classes, the background may need to be much longer, and your instructor may want the historical comments to be limited to the history of research efforts on a very particular scientific problem. At the high school level, historical information will be more general.

Quoting dictionary definitions is something grammar school students commonly do, but it is bad form for more advanced students. If you are using a common term, a definition is not necessary. If you are using a specialized term, then it is better to quote a definition from a technical source (such as a text) with an appropriate reference citation rather than from a dictionary.

In the Background section do not go into any specific calculations or measurements. Do not discuss anything that actually happened during the experiment. All of that comes later. Keep your comments general but informative.

1. History

   If your experiment relates at all to principles discovered in the past, always begin with a bit of history, but make your comments brief and specific to the theory or law you are working with. This is not a history paper, and it is not the place to paste in a load of quasi-irrelevant information you copied from a website. Focus on how and when the law you are investigating was discovered and the vital steps of discovery that inform the work you are presently engaged in. A line or two of biographical information about the individuals behind your theory is appropriate, but avoid extended, random biographical information that is not directly relevant to your experiment. Always cite your sources using the formatting standards your instructor requires (see the References section in the next chapter).

2. Theory

   Describe the theory your experiment is based on. If the theory includes equations, state and explain them here. Also explain what they will be used for in your experiment and what the variables mean in each one. If you need to express equations in different forms to assist with your description of your theoretical approach to this work, do so, but do not describe the tedious details of the mathematics. For example, it is appropriate to write:

   "Newton's Second Law of Motion, $F = ma$, can also be written as $a = \frac{F}{m}$."

   But do not write:

   "Newton's Second Law of Motion is $F = ma$. If we divide both sides by m and cancel the m's on the right-hand side we get $a = \frac{F}{m}$."

   Remember, your reader is an intelligent person who is mathematically competent and has a working scientific vocabulary. Your reader doesn't need an explanation from Pre-Algebra about how to solve an equation for a variable. On the other hand, if you used unique or sophisticated solution methods these should be described in some detail.

3. Overview of experimental plan

   In a few sentences, outline the general approach you followed in the experiment and the major pieces of equipment or apparatus you used. The goal here is that the reader has a basic idea of what is going on so that your description later of the detailed procedure will make sense. If, after reading this part, the reader still does not know why you did certain things, then this section is not adequately developed.

   If you are using a theory to make predictions, explain how this will be done. It is appropriate to do this here, after the experimental plan has been explained.

4. Hypothesis

   Conclude the Background section with a specific statement of your experimental hypothesis, written in the past tense. The hypothesis statement will only be present in hypothesis-driven experiments, where your team forms a hypothesis and then performs the experiment to confirm or disconfirm that hypothesis. By contrast, in a discovery-driven experiment (such as a dissection in biology), there is no hypothesis. There is simply the goal of the work that you stated previously in the Purpose section.

4.6 Experimental Procedure

In this section describe *what you did* but not *what happened*. Begin this section with a list of the equipment and supplies used in the experiment. Then describe your experimental procedures and methods in detail. Watch your verb tenses and strive to make your methods crystal clear to the reader. This will be easier to do well if you generally avoid using pronouns. As described in the previous chapter, some instructors require this section to be written in the passive voice.

Do not present data in this section, and do not get into describing or interpreting your results.

4.7 Results

In this section, describe *what happened*, that is, what the results were of the procedure you just described. Present your data in tables. Label and title them, and refer to each of them in order in the text before they appear. If you were required to make qualitative observations during the course of the experiment, describe them here. Do not begin interpreting your results here; that is to be done in the Discussion section. Here just state what happened.

Don't forget to present every value of every variable. Often there is a single value (such as a mass, a height, or a concentration) that is used in multiple trials. If there are only one or two such values, they probably aren't worth making a table for, and this makes it easy to forget to state them at all. Also, make note that data values can never simply appear on a page. They must either be stated in a complete sentence or placed in a table. And always, always state units of measure. Every time.

4.8 Discussion

Before getting to the details on the content for the Discussion section of your report, we need to establish how to approach the calculation universally and incorrectly referred to as the *experimental error*. I have a different term I like to use, and which I encourage other teachers to use. Of course, you should use the terminology preferred by your own instructor. We will discuss this terminology first and then move on to the other details of the Discussion section.

Percent Difference

One of the conventional calculations in laboratory science courses is the so-called *experimental error*. Experimental error is typically defined as the difference between the predicted value (or accepted value) and the experimental value, expressed as a percentage of the predicted value, or

$$\text{experimental error} = \frac{|\text{predicted/accepted value} - \text{experimental value}|}{\text{predicted value}} \times 100\%$$

Although the term *experimental error* is widely used, it is a poor choice of words. When there is a mismatch between theory and experiment, error in the experiment may not be the source of the difference. Often, it is the theory that is found wanting—this is how science advances.

I now prefer to use the phrase *percent difference* to describe the value computed by the above equation. When quantitative results can be compared to quantitative predictions or accepted values, students should compute the percent difference as

$$\text{percent difference} = \frac{|\text{predicted/accepted value} - \text{experimental value}|}{\text{predicted value}} \times 100\%$$

As you see, the calculation is the same. This issue is simply about what we will call this calculation. Again, if your instructor wants you to stick with the conventional use of "experimental error," you should do so. But in the rest of this manual, including the example reports in Chapter 9, I will use the term *percent difference*.[1] In Section 6.4, we will look at a specific case where error originates in the theoretical model and not in the experiment.

Discussion Section Content

The goal for the Discussion section is to analyze and discuss your results, explain whether your hypothesis was confirmed, spell out what you learned, and judge whether your results were definitive or inconclusive, regardless of whether the hypothesis was confirmed.

The outline below will work successfully for many standard lab reports. However, the issues addressed in this section do not necessarily need to be treated in this exact order. More advanced writers should feel free to tailor the structure of this section to suit your own work.

1. If your experiment involved calculating predicted values, present these. Use a table for these values unless there are only one or two values. Always state the units.

2. If your report includes any graphs or diagrams that are discussed in this section, you should present these next. As with tables, graphs, and figures referred to earlier, label these, title them, and refer to them in the text. Comment on your graph, its characteristics, what it tells you, and whether it appears as expected. For graphs or diagrams that occur in longer, more sophisticated reports (in which the Discussion section is much more than just a paragraph or two), placement

1 I ceased using the term "experimental error" in early 2013. Earlier editions of my texts include that language. The language is different in newer texts.

at the beginning of the Discussion section is not necessary. Place them where appropriate in the body of your discussion.

3. If your experiment was hypothesis-driven, proceed next to present the percent difference figure(s) you calculated for your experimental results. Calculate the percent difference using the standard equation:

$$\text{percent difference} = \frac{|\text{predicted/accepted value} - \text{experimental value}|}{\text{predicted value}} \times 100\%$$

   If there are more than one or two percent difference values, place them all in a table. For students who are new to writing lab reports, it is a good idea to show the percent difference equation just to make it clear to the reader that you know what you are doing.

   In more advanced classes, the instructor may require you to estimate the experimental uncertainty in your data. Present that information here along with the analysis to support your uncertainty values. (Details on experimental uncertainty are discussed in Section 5.7.)

4. Next, discuss the percent difference and whether it is a reasonable amount of difference to expect for your experiment based on the type of equipment used, how much time was spent, and so on. If the results were excellent and the difference was very low, then you don't really need to try to explain it. Just say that the results conformed very closely to your prediction. However, if the difference figures are significant, then your next task is to discuss factors that may have caused the difference. This includes identifying sources of error in the experiment or sources of approximation in your theoretical model. (This will be discussed in Sections 6.3–6.6.)

5. Finally, discuss whether your hypothesis was confirmed and whether your results were definitive. These are separate issues. Your hypothesis might have been completely incorrect, but your experimental results might have been so consistent that you have now a clear idea of what a correct hypothesis would have been. Conversely, your hypothesis might have been correctly formed from the theory but your results were too inconsistent to tell if the hypothesis was confirmed by the experiment. The most desirable case, of course, is to have consistent, definitive results that confirm the hypothesis you started out with. But to have a successful experiment, the results mainly need to be definitive so that you learn something specific about the scientific principles under study.

4.9 Conclusion

In this section, summarize your results, how definitive they were, and their relationship to the hypothesis. Wrap it up with an overall judgment about how successful the experiment was. As a reminder, a science lab report is not the place to express your personal feelings such as how much fun you had and so on. It is appropriate to comment on why the experiment is interesting from a scientific point of view (this would be better placed in the background), but leave your personal feelings out of it. (Feel free to tell your teacher in person about how much fun you had, but leave it out of the report!) Keep your comments strictly on your experiment, your findings, and your recommendations for improvements to the experiment or for future research.

As part of your judgment about the success of the experiment, it is appropriate to suggest specific ways the experiment could be improved, or areas where further research could be conducted. If your percent difference figures were higher than you thought they should have been, you should try to suggest ways that the experiment could be improved, thus reducing percent difference values for students in the future.

4.10 References

Younger students may not have very many references in lab reports, but more advanced students often will. Scientific research articles almost always refer to other articles, or occasionally to books. They almost never refer to websites, because these are not regarded as scholarly sources. Your instructor will probably have requirements for the kinds of sources you may cite.

Even if you are a younger student, if you use any outside resources in the development of your report, such as a technical or history reference for your background section, or a technical website to help you interpret your data, these sources must be cited at the end of the paper in the References section. You may be used to using MLA formatting for citations on your humanities papers, but MLA formatting and the MLA-style Works Cited page are *not* used in technical papers. Instead, you number your references at the end of the paper in the References section, and in the text you refer to those references in one of two ways: using a superscript, like this[1], or parentheses, like this (1).

Even though research scientists typically don't refer to websites, high school students often do. If you need to cite a website, use the MLA formatting for it that you are probably already familiar with (or will be soon!), without any indentations.

Formatting details and examples are presented in Section 5.9. For books and journal articles, formatting standards vary a bit among the different scientific journals. The examples in the next chapter illustrate two different common formats. Your instructor may require a particular format, or may leave the choice up to you. Regardless of which format you use, make sure you use it consistently.

Chapter 5
Section Content Detail

In this chapter you will find more detailed descriptions of the content for each of the sections in your report. You will probably find the Discussion section to be especially helpful with its extended treatment of data analysis. The topic of data analysis is so important that we will go into it even further in Chapter 6.

5.1 Heading

Students have sometimes asked me if the time of the experiment should be included in the heading. The short answer is no. If the time of your experiment is significant, such as in the case of astronomical observations, then the times of your observations will be recorded in the data and will not be recorded here in the heading.

If your entire class performed the experiment as one large group, instead of listing the team members' names individually, simply write something like "Chemistry class, E period."

5.2 Abstract

Writing a good abstract takes practice. Your goal is to describe your entire experiment, your results, and your conclusions in a single paragraph. To do this, you write in extremely blunt terms, leaving out all detail, and summarizing your results in a few sentences. Your last sentence summarizes the significance of your work.

Most technical papers have abstracts, but in high school they are typically only used in accelerated or upper-level science classes. If your instructor requires your report to have an abstract, he or she should direct you to some example abstracts to study. Three of the example reports in Chapter 9 include abstracts.

5.3 Purpose

As described previously, the purpose of experiments in science classes is typically either to collect data and compare them to predictions derived from scientific theory, or to explore an unknown phenomenon and make observations. There is a third type as well. Your instructor may wish for you to first try to discover a scientific principle on your own, and then make predictions from it, collect data, and compare your results to your predictions. This third type is just a combination of the first two types into one experiment.

If you will be collecting data, it is unlikely that the purpose of your experiment is merely to collect the data and stop there. More likely, the purpose will be to measure certain values, perhaps perform computations with them, and compare your results to some other values (and, of course, discuss what you find). By performing this comparison, you are either validating your data or the values you are comparing to (depending on which one is most credible).

The values you compare your data to can come from various sources. Often they will be the results of calculations you make based on a scientific theory. Or, they could be *standard* or *accepted values* that you look up in a reference such as the *CRC Handbook of Physics and Chemistry*. Or again, they could be values supplied by a manufacturer. In any case, values of variables you determine by your experiment are called the *experimental values*. Values you calculate from a theory are called *predicted values* (because you are using the theory to predict what the values will be), or *theoretical values*. Values obtained from a scientific reference source are usually called *standard* or *accepted values*. Values you obtain from a manufacture can be called *manufacturer's values*.

Briefly, here are a few examples of experiments involving these different sources of values to compare your data to. If you measured the speed of a car after it rolls down a hill and compared that speed to one you calculated using energy principles, your calculated value is a predicted (or theoretical) value. If you measured the density of a substance and compared it to a density you found in a mechanical engineering handbook or materials reference, the value you look up is a standard or accepted value. If you measured resistor values and compared them to values specified by the color code on the resistor, you can call the value specified by the color code the manufacturer's value.

5.4 Background

One of the goals of the Background section is to show that you are an active participant in the wonderful scientific project of discovery that has been going on for thousands of years. You want to demonstrate to your instructor that you know where these scientific ideas originated, what the scientific principles are as we understand them today, and what some of the major milestones were in the history of scientific research that might relate particularly to your experiment. But as stated previously, don't go overboard. Keep your historical comments relevant and brief so you can move right on to explaining the theory behind your work.

If you have several equations to present in this section, you may find it helpful to number them to make it easier to refer to them. In the "Investigating Charles' Law" sample report included in Chapter 9, major equations are numbered to allow for easy reference to them in the text. Although I numbered the equations in that example for instructional purposes, note that numbering equations is only necessary when you need to make repeated references to several different equations.

A few more words on vocabulary are in order. Basic scientific terms and equipment (e.g., volume, titration, temperature, triple-beam balance, etc.) do not need to be defined or explained unless they themselves are the subject of the report. This might be the case if you were investigating a particularly complex piece of apparatus, such as a laser. Specialized or more sophisticated terms (e.g., spectrograph, electrolyte, specific heat capacity, etc.) should be explained or defined. But as mentioned before, don't quote a dictionary. If you like the idea of quoting a source for a definition, quote a text or an authoritative source from the scientific literature.

5.5 Experimental Procedure

Begin this section by itemizing the equipment used in the experiment. Begin with a phrase such as "Equipment and materials used in this experiment were:" and then list the items right down the left margin of the page (not in sentences). Include everything used in the experiment. Do not use bullets or numbers. Be sure to include any minor supplies used such as tape or paper. Be specific with types of equipment. Specify the manufacturer and model number of all electronic equipment and all major pieces of equipment. For generic items not designed for this work (such as materials used for leveling a table or blocking out the light from a window), describe the items generically, not specifically. Use capital letters only for proper names. Do not use articles (a, an) and include quantities (in parentheses) only when more than one of the items was used. Do not list people as equipment. Refer to the the four example reports in Chapter 9 to see what such a list looks like and how to refer to specific types of equipment.

After the equipment list, begin describing everything you did. If the reasons for certain procedures are not clear, explain them. If the actual experimental procedure was short, or involved only a few steps, it is acceptable to describe the procedure in a paragraph. More complex procedures will need more complex descriptions.

Start at the beginning and don't leave anything out. In this section, you should include enough detail in your procedure so that another scientist could replicate your experiment. If you repeated trials so many times, say how many and why. If you had a specific criterion for determining if your data were acceptable, state it. If you did something over because your data were not acceptable, say so. If there were preliminaries to be performed before the experiment proper was commenced, state them. Describe all measurements made, but do not report the values here. (They go in the next section.) Remember, as always, to write as clearly and succinctly as possible.

When explaining the procedure, you should include details that are significant and relevant but leave out details that are obvious, trivial, or pedantic. If learning how to use the apparatus is a significant part of the activity, such as is often the case in introductory Physical Science or Chemistry courses, then you should include enough detail in your procedural explanations to show that you correctly used and calibrated the apparatus. In higher-level courses, students should increasingly focus on the rationale behind their methods and leave out trivial details.

Here are two examples of sentences to illustrate the right amount of detail.

Too much trivial detail:

> "We went to the table at the front of the room, obtained 23.5 g of salt, carried it back to our table and added it to 155 mL of water in a beaker."

Appropriate detail:

> "We added 23.5 g of salt to 155 mL of water."

Good organization of information and clarity of explanation are important in describing an experimental procedure. You must learn how to write a description that makes sense and is understandable to someone who was not present during the experiment. While learning this skill, you may find it helpful to read your descriptions to a parent, a roommate, or a peer who is not in your science class to see if what you have written is clear and makes sense.

When describing laboratory procedures that are repetitive, such as multiple tests that involve the same sequence of steps on each sample, do not repeat the procedure over and over multiple times. Instead, number the repeating steps in your procedure and the simply state something like "Steps 4 through 8 were repeated for sample volumes of 20.0, 30.0, and 40.0 mL."

As discussed in Chapter 3, do not write your procedure in the imperative mood as if you were writing instructions or a recipe. Instead, write in past tense or the passive voice describing what you and your team members did. Do not identify specific team members' names with specific tasks. Refer instead to actions performed by "the team," "a team member," or "the group."

If diagrams, figures, or photographs are used in this section, label them as Figure 1., Figure 2., etc., title each one, and refer to each of them, in order, in the text.

If you have to do any part of the experiment over for any reason (contamination, bad data, etc.), you need to describe, as briefly as possible, what happened and what you had to do over.

5.6 Results

Every single measurement you made needs to be presented, either in a table or in a paragraph. Do not just write random values on the page. Either incorporate the values into a sentence, or if there are more than two or three values, place them in one or more tables. As described in detail in the Section 3.4, each table, graph, and figure needs to be labeled and titled using standard formatting. Each one also needs to be mentioned in the text of the report. You cannot have one of these elements in a report without referring to it in a sentence.

It is important that you present all data using the same units of measure that were used to make the original measurement. A reader should be able to follow your work all the way through, verifying all of the calculations and uncovering any mistakes that might have been made. Your presentation of the calculations and results should allow for this.

If you computed means of data values, or converted units of measure to other units, it is appropriate to place additional rows or columns in your tables to accommodate these values. However, if you are performing more extensive statistical analysis on your data, then these statistics should be presented separately in the Discussion section.

If your experiment involved a large amount of data, your instructor may prefer your data to be shown in an appendix or submitted electronically instead of listed directly in the text. In that case, the only content in the Results section might be a reference to where the data are to be found and a table with appropriate summary values.

5.7 Discussion

There is a lot to say about the Discussion section. It is the heart of your report and will probably affect your grade more than any other section. Error analysis, which is an important part of this section, will be discussed at even greater length in the next chapter.

Key goals for the discussion section include:

- Be economical—Work hard to write as succinctly as possible. However, do not be too succinct. Your discussion—and your report in general—needs to present a complete and thorough description of the experiment. Leave out the rambling sentences that don't add specific technical content to the document. Include all of the detail necessary for your report to be thorough all the way through.
- Be clear—Eliminate vague terms and references and make your comments as clear as possible.
- Be focused—Get to the real issues, which are your hypothesis, your results, and how they compare. Or in the case of discovery-driven reports, the detailed, systematic description of what you found in your investigation.
- Include both quantitative and qualitative analysis—Analyze shapes of graphs and percent differences, as well as other observations you made.

Your discussion needs to follow a logical, orderly flow. The sequence outlined below is a good guideline you can follow for hypothesis-driven reports:

1. First, set the stage for your comments by citing the predicted values you calculated (if any) that you will use in the analysis. You have already explained in the Background section the equations you used to obtain these values. Unless there are only one or two values, the predicted values need to go in a table.

2. Next, if a graphical representation of your data is appropriate, present that graph (or those graphs) here. As with every table, graph, and figure, refer to the graph in the text of the report. Unless this is one of your first reports, it is likely that your graph will need to show both predicted and experimental values. (See Chapter 7 for detailed instructions on how to do this.)

3. Next, present an estimate of the uncertainty in your experimental data. This item applies to advanced classes that require you to address experimental uncertainty in your data. There is no such thing as an exact measurement; *all* measurements involve uncertainty. If you are making measurements with fine enough resolution, you will always be able to see variation in your measured values, which means your measurements will always have a certain degree of uncertainty built into them. There are various metrics you can use to express the uncertainty, but there is no commonly recognized standard. So what many scientists do is use the sample standard deviation ($\pm 1s$) as a representation of the experimental uncertainty. Your instructor may require you to address this by showing uncertainty bars on your graphs (and explaining them) or by quoting this value in your data tables. Either way, this would apply only if you have at least several data values for each measurement condition so that you can calculate the sample standard deviation of the measurements for each measurement condition.

   When dealing with uncertainty, you have several measurements for the same measurement condition, so you will typically calculate the mean of these values to quote as your result, with the uncertainty figures representing one standard deviation above and below the mean (mean $\pm$ $1s$). You will have a different uncertainty value for each measurement condition, so if you took enough data to plot, say, six different points on a graph, that means you have six sets of data. Each one of these data sets will have a mean and a sample standard deviation to use for the uncertainty for that measurement condition. With this many uncertainty values, you will need to present them in a table.

   When quoting your uncertainty using values written in scientific notation, use the same power of ten in your uncertainty as you used in your mean value. Here are a couple of examples showing how to quote the uncertainty:

   "The acceleration was found to be 3.23×10^{-2} m/s^2 $\pm$ 0.04×10^{-2} m/s^2."

   "The acceleration was found to be 0.0323 m/s^2, with an uncertainty (s) of 0.0004 m/s^2."

4. Next, present your percent difference figures. If you are in an introductory science course (ninth or possibly tenth grade), you should quote the percent difference equation in your text. Here it is again:

$$\text{percent difference} = \frac{|\text{predicted/accepted value} - \text{experimental value}|}{\text{predicted value}} \times 100\%$$

   To quote this equation, write, "Percent difference values were calculated as…", followed by the equation. For students in more advanced classes, your instructor will assume you know this equation and you can simply present your difference figures. Again, if you have more than one or two, these go in a table.

5. Next, get into the heart of this section, which is to compare your experimental values to the values you predicted from the theory. Be as quantitative as possible, using your data, graphs, and calculations of percent difference.

Do not make the mistake of stating that your results are "wrong" because they do not match the predicted values. Analyzing your results is not about whether your results are right or wrong; it is about how closely they match the predictions, both in their values and in the trend in the data (represented by the shape of the curve you see when you display the data and the predicted values graphically).

Rather than thinking of your results as right or wrong, you should look for specific ways to compare your results to the values you predicted. Some examples of the types of comments you can make include:

> "The data closely match predicted values."

This is appropriate to say when the percent difference figures are very low.

> "The data are all above [or below] the predicted values."

This type of result indicates a consistent bias in one direction that you should explain (probably certain conditions or factors which have not been accounted for). For more on this, see Random and Systematic Error, Section 6.3.

> "The data vary both above and below predicted values, indicating inconsistency and variations in whatever was causing the difference."

This result is probably due to inaccuracies in the measurements.

> "The data are linear, but have a different slope than the predicted curve."

> "The data are linear and have the right slope, but are shifted vertically from the predicted curve."

> "The data are [or are not] linear [or inverse, quadratic, etc.] as predicted."

In other words, the curve has (or does not have) the predicted shape.

6. The next main task is to attempt to explain the factors that may have led to the percent differences you have. If your percent differences are small enough so that the predicted values fall within the boundaries of the experimental uncertainty, then the differences don't need much explanation. (If your uncertainty is large, that means your data are inconsistent, which may need explaining, but that is a separate issue.) In this case you can simply state: "the experimental results match the predictions within experimental uncertainty."

   Regarding percent difference, for typical experiments with equipment available in student labs, a percent difference figure in the range of 5–10% is pretty good. Generally, if your percent difference values are below 5% using student lab equipment, then your results match your predicted values very well.

   If your percent difference is larger than the uncertainty (often the case with high school experiments), or if you were not required to estimate the uncertainty, then you will need to make an effort to explain your percent difference values. This will require you to identify possible sources of the difference, including sources of error in your measurements. State the reasonable possibilities your group considered for explaining the difference. Then assess each one by explaining why it does or does not fit the observations. Do not waste your discussion on insignificant or irrelevant sources of error. Consider what the effects would be of the error sources you propose, and whether they would produce the kind of error you actually have. Possibilities to consider include human error (explain), faulty procedures (identify them), faulty measurement technique (discover how it was at fault and explain it), faulty or inadequate equipment (specify), and unanticipated interference from outside sources (identify such sources and explain how they affected the measurements). Again, you can't just list these in your report generically or randomly. You must explain specifically why and how a possible source of error pertains to your particular case. It is not adequate merely to record a long list of possible sources of error; you must identify specific possibilities and comment on each one.

It is very important to distinguish between factors that could have been significant sources of error and those that could not have been. In this regard, consider the percent difference, and consider what kinds of percentages of error in measurements would have had to be present in order to cause a given error in the outcome.

It is *inappropriate* to attribute your percent difference to the possibility that you made errors in the calculations used to generate predicted values. If you made calculation errors, you need to correct them, obtain correct predictions, and refigure the percent differences. If your percent difference is very high, you should certainly double-check your calculations. If there are several members in your team, each member should separately calculate the predicted values. Group members can then compare their predicted values to make sure everyone agrees on what the predicted values should be.

7. Finally, in this section you will also need to address any discussion questions the instructor supplied as part of the lab exercise.

5.8 Conclusion

As mentioned previously, one of the things you should address in the conclusion is your ideas about how the experiment could be improved. However, avoid simply criticizing the quality of the equipment you used and recommending that better results could be achieved with better equipment. This is always the case! It is always possible to come up with more accurate and more precise equipment (unless you are already using the finest equipment in the world, which is unlikely in a high school or undergraduate science class), so experimental results can always be improved this way. Thus, this is not an interesting thing to say. Your instructor has provided particular equipment based on the school or college budget and on the goals of the course. Your task is to try to think of ways the experiment could be improved given the particular equipment that was available. Try to suggest changes to the procedure, additional materials that would make the given equipment work better, and so on.

5.9 References

The examples below illustrate two different common formats for citing references. When citing journal articles, numbers in bold print refer to the volume number of the journal. The numbers that come next are page numbers (either the page where the article begins, or all of the pages the article takes up) followed by the year in parentheses. Journal names are usually abbreviated unless they are very short.

Here are actual examples of references for a journal article and a book taken from one of the major science journals. This particular journal uses in-text parentheses like this (1) to point the reader to the appropriate reference.

1. C. Pfleiderer, S. R. Julian, G. G. Louzarich, Non-Fermi-liquid nature of the normal state of itinerant-electron ferromagnets, *Nature* **414**, 427 (2001).

2. N. W. Ashcroft, N. D. Mermin, *Solid State Physics* (Holt, Rinehart and Winston, NY, 1976).

Here are two more actual examples of references, again for a journal article and a book, taken from another of the major science journals. This particular journal uses superscripts like this[1] or this[4,7] to point the reader to the appropriate reference.

1. Zhang, H., Stallock, J. P., Ng, J. C., Reinhard, C., & Neufeld, T. P. Regulation of cellular growth by the *Drosophila* target of rapamycin dTOR. *Genes Dev.* **14**, 2712-2724 (2000).
2. Brilliantov, N. V. & Pöschel, T. *Kinetic Theory of Granular Gases* (Oxford University Press, 2004).

Chapter 6
Analyzing and Discussing Results

In this chapter, we want to go even deeper into the analysis you perform on your results. You will probably not need to consider the things in this chapter during the fall of your freshman year of high school. But as you learn more about performing and documenting scientific work, your instructor will want you to begin to incorporate these more advanced considerations into your writing.

As I mentioned before, the analysis and discussion are the heart of your report. But before we continue with this topic, there are three other technical matters we need to address. We will treat these first, and then continue our discussion about analysis in Section 6.4. The more advanced you are in your scientific coursework, the more probable it is that your instructor will want you to be able to engage in sophisticated error analysis as part of your lab exercise. Accelerated high school freshmen, upper-level high school students, and all college undergraduates should study the more advanced material in Sections 6.3 through 6.6 closely.

6.1 Outliers

An outlier is a data value that is widely separated from all the other values. Although you might be tempted simply to toss these values out and use the other ones, you can't do this without an explanation. For younger students who have not studied statistics, it is usually acceptable to state why you think the outliers can be ignored, and then ignore them and move on. Straightforward reasons might be, for example, the equipment wasn't warmed up yet, we weren't being careful enough, we made a mistake and had to do the trial over, we realized we had certain settings wrong, and so on. If anything like this happened during your experiment, you should have noted it in your lab journal and in your experimental procedure. If there is no reason to reject these values, then you can't reject them and you should include them in your calculations and your analysis.

Note that if you have an entire set of bad data that has to be taken over again, these values are not outliers. Outliers are exceptional data points in an otherwise good data set.

6.2 Accuracy and Precision

There is an important difference between the terms *accuracy* and *precision*. Data are accurate when the scientist uses accurate measurement instruments and avoids making errors. To have accurate data, the scientist needs to avoid error in the experimental setup, experimental procedure, use and reading of the measurement instruments, and recording of the data. Further, the equipment all needs to be operating properly. The scientist must also avoid error caused by extraneous factors that have nothing to do with his or her experiment such as radiation, the rotation of the earth, and biological contamination. This is accomplished by having good procedures. Avoiding all possible errors is probably impossible, although it is possible to minimize them by good experimental technique and good equipment. In sum, if you avoid errors, your data are as accurate as they can be.

On the other hand, data are precise when you use measurement instrumentation with a high resolution, which means that the instrument can distinguish between measurements at a very fine level. In other words, high-precision instruments provide measurements with many *significant digits.*[1] Using low-grade equipment with low resolution will result in data values that are rounded off, reducing the precision of the measurement. This rounding may mask other important errors caused by experimental inaccuracies.

Notice that precise measurements can be inaccurate and vice versa. You can have a very precise tool that reads lengths to the nearest micrometer, but if the tool is poorly manufactured, damaged, or out of calibration all its very precise measurements will be inaccurate. Likewise, you can make very accurate measurements, but with an imprecise measurement tool you will not be able to see the true value of the measurement. For example, if a length you are trying to measure is 0.05521 meters but your instrument only reads to the nearest millimeter, your measurement will come out to 0.055 meters. The value 0.055 meters is quite accurate, but since it only has two significant digits it is not very precise.

In summary, since lack of accuracy and lack of precision both result in measurements that are different from the true value, they both contribute to the percent difference in your measurements.

All experiments contain inaccuracies, and thus, all data contain some error due to these inaccuracies. Moreover, all experimental data are obtained with measurement tools with limited precision, so data are always limited in their precision as well. For this reason, experimental data can never match predicted values *exactly*. First, there is no such thing as an exact measurement, since all measurements have finite precision. Second, the lower the sophistication of the lab equipment used, the more likely it is that the data will contain inaccuracies that add to the percent difference. A good experimental scientist spends a lot of time eliminating sources of inaccuracy from his or her equipment and measurement techniques. If the scientist could eliminate inaccuracy entirely (which, again, is probably impossible), then the match between experimental values and predicted values would still be limited by the precision of the measurement instruments.

This all influences how you write when you are discussing the difference between your measured values and your predictions. Do not expect your measurements to match your predictions exactly; they won't. This means you should not say in your analysis that your results are "wrong" because they don't match the predicted values. As stated in the previous chapter, it's not about whether your results are right or wrong; it is about how closely they match the predictions, both in their values and in the trend in the data.

6.3 Random Error and Systematic Error

There are two main types of error in experimental measurements, *random error* and *systematic error.* As you move through the science program and get into more advanced courses, your instructor will probably want you to learn to distinguish between random and systematic error and incorporate these concepts into your discussion.

Random errors are caused by unknown and unpredictable fluctuations in the experimental setup. Examples of random error would be changes in the apparatus due to temperature fluctuations in the room, vibrations or wind that influence the measurement in a random fashion, or electronic noise that influences the readings in your instruments. When you calculate and discuss the uncertainty in your measurements, you are discussing the random error that caused your measurements to fluctuate randomly around the mean value.

1 A detailed explanation of significant digits (also known as significant figures) goes beyond the scope of this *Handbook*, but can be found in any introductory physics or chemistry text.

Systematic errors are errors that bias the experimental results in one direction, and are usually caused by equipment defects, miscalibration of measurement instruments, or an experimenter who consistently misreads or misuses the instruments in the same way. Usually, when discussing systematic error, we are talking about problems that could be eliminated by proper use, calibration, and operation of the equipment.

Your percent difference values can be influenced by factors you did not take into account in your predictions, and the result can be percent difference values that look like they include systematic error. A common example of this is motion experiments in physics that do not take friction into account. If you make predictions in a mechanical system without taking friction into account, your results will all be biased in the same way relative to your measurements. This is *not* an "experimental error"; it is the result of using approximations in your theoretical modeling of the experiment (our next topic). However, it is a contributor to your percent difference values and could play a role in your discussion. We will consider this in an example in Section 6.5.

6.4 Percent Differences Can Come From Your Model

Scientific *theories* or *laws* are *models* that we used to describe and make predictions. If a theory is a good model, it will lead to very accurate predictions that can be accurately confirmed by well-designed experiments. But if the theoretical model contains approximations, experimental results can differ from predictions enough to cause significant percent difference values. In such a case, the experimental procedures can be flawless and the measurements highly accurate. The percent difference values that result are not a result of the experiment; they are caused by approximations in the theoretical model. Back in Section 4.7, I explained why I discontinued use of the common term *experimental error* and adopted the term *percent difference* in its place. The scenario I have just described illustrates why.

Here is a specific example to illustrate. The example involves a bit of math that is familiar to students who have had Pre-Calculus. If you are not yet in Pre-Calculus, just try to follow along as well as you can without getting hung up on the math.

We begin with the setup: Physicists often use the so-called *small angle approximation* to simplify the mathematics in routine calculations. This comes up all the time in geometric optics, simple harmonic motion, and other topics in physics. The small angle approximation says that when working with angles measured in radians,[2] the following holds for small angles:

For small θ, $\sin\theta \cong \theta$.

To illustrate just how good this approximation is, look at the values in this table:

θ, degrees	θ, radians	$\sin\theta$	difference (%)
10.000	0.17453	0.17365	0.504
1.0000	0.017453	0.017452	0.00508
0.10000	0.0017453	0.0017453	< 0.0000001

2 If you haven't been introduced to radians yet, here is the basic idea: Instead of measuring angles in degrees, we use the radius of the circle wrapped along the rim of the circle as a way to measure angles. A length of one radius laid along the circumference of a circle defines an angle of 1 radian, which is approximately 57.3°. In physics and math, the measure of angles is typically denoted by the Greek letter theta, θ (the "th" sound in Greek).

As you see, even at angles as large as 10°, the difference between the measure of the angle (in radians) and the sine of the angle is only around half a percent. For smaller angles, the difference gets very small, and the small angle approximation becomes very useful—trigonometric equations can be approximated by much simpler algebraic equations by replacing $\sin\theta$ with θ. This is *very* handy.

Now for the example: Let's say you have an apparatus that can measure angles to the nearest 0.01°. You are doing a simple experiment in optics involving the angle of an expanding laser beam. The angle of the expanding beam on one side of the beam path is 30.00°. You use the small angle approximation in your calculations. Let's see what you will measure and how it comes out.

$$30.00° = 0.5236 \text{ radians}$$

$$\sin(0.5236 \text{ radians}) = 0.5000$$

So in your calculations, you are going to use the angle measure of 0.5236 radians in place of the sine of the angle, which is 0.5000. The percent difference between these two is 4.7%. This difference is not an experimental error! Your experiment accurately measured angles down to 0.01 degrees. The difference was caused by your model, which stretched the boundaries of the small angle approximation and led to a difference between prediction and result of almost 5%.

The punch line from this section is that differences between your results and your predictions might be due to errors in your measurements or experimental procedure, or they may be due to approximations or other deficiencies in your model. The first is an *experimental error*; the second is not.

6.5 Examples of Analysis

Example 1

Consider the following actual example taken from one of my classes:

In an experiment involving the gravitational potential energy (E_G) of a small car rolling down hill on a track, students found the measured velocity of the car after it rolled down the track to be lower than the predicted velocity by 31.7%. The students determined the experimental velocity by timing the car with a stopwatch as it traveled a known distance on a level surface at the bottom of the hill. In seeking to explain this large percent difference, the students first assumed that there might have been errors in the distance and time measurements used to determine the velocity.

The students should have considered whether it was reasonable that the distance or time measurements could contain enough error to cause a percent difference of 31.7%. It is indeed possible that there was a significant error in the time measurement if it was measured by a human using a stop watch, but it is not reasonable that a distance measurement would be in error this much unless a gross error was made. In fact, in the particular case we are considering, two human timers were used as a double check on their accuracy, and the car was traveling slowly enough that errors in timing should not have been this large. An error of 10% or even 20% was believable, but not 30%. We needed to keep looking for the source of this percent difference.

What if there was an error in the amount of kinetic energy (E_K) used to calculate the predicted velocity? The kinetic energy was calculated from conservation of energy principles as $E_{K,f} = E_{G,i} = mgh$.

If you have studied introductory physics, you know that we can use these energy values to predict what the velocity of the car will be at the bottom of the hill, and that the predicted velocity will be equal to $v = \sqrt{\frac{2E_{K,f}}{m}}$, where the kinetic energy involved (E_{Kf}) is equal to the gravitational potential energy ($E_{G,i} = mgh$) the car had at the top of the hill. If our measured value was correct but our prediction of E_{Kf} was wrong, it would require a 114% error in the E_{Kf} value for the measured velocity to appear to be in error by 31.7%. (The math involved to work this out is a bit tricky, but you might enjoy the challenge of attempting to work it out for yourself.) Could the mass or height measurements have been in error by over 100%? Obviously not.

Thus, some other major factor must have been affecting the experimental result. In the case of the car on the track, it is almost certain that friction was the major contributor to the error, because the portion of the original energy converted to heat due to friction would be deducted from the car's energy as it descended, and the kinetic energy the car had at the bottom would be lower than the original energy by that amount. In other experiments, other factors would need to be explored such as measurement errors, limitations to the accuracy of measurements, inaccurate apparatus, interference from outside factors, heat loss to the environment, or other factors. And as mentioned in Section 5.7, calculation errors are never a legitimate explanation because the student should discover them and correct them before they are written into the report.

(You might be interested to know that it was in fact friction causing the error in this example. We figured this out by using digital timers to time the car over a much shorter distance, shorter so that we didn't lose as much energy from friction. This reduced the percent difference dramatically.)

Example 2

Let's look at another example. Table 6-1 shows the data values used to construct the graph in Figure 6-1, which could represent the data resulting from a certain experiment. I made the titles and labels on the graph generic, but all your graphs must have variable names and units shown on both axes, as discussed in Chapter 7.

Variable A (units)	Variable B, predicted (units)	Variable B, experimental (units)
1.00	2.00	2.30
2.00	5.00	5.60
3.00	10.0	10.9
4.00	17.0	17.8
5.00	26.0	28.0

Table 6-1. Data for the example plot in Figure 6-1.

Now consider this question: Do the test results indicate a successful experiment because the curves are similar and close together, or an unsuccessful experiment because the experimental curve does not exactly match the predicted curve? This is the fundamental question that all experimenters have to answer when analyzing their data. Because uncertainty is always present in experimental data, the appropriate question to ask during experimental analysis is not whether the experimental values match the predicted values exactly. Remember, there is no such thing as an exact measurement. Instead, the experimentalist should determine how close the experimental values are to the predicted values. To do this, both qualitative (words) and quantitative (numbers) comparisons should be made between predicted and experimental values.

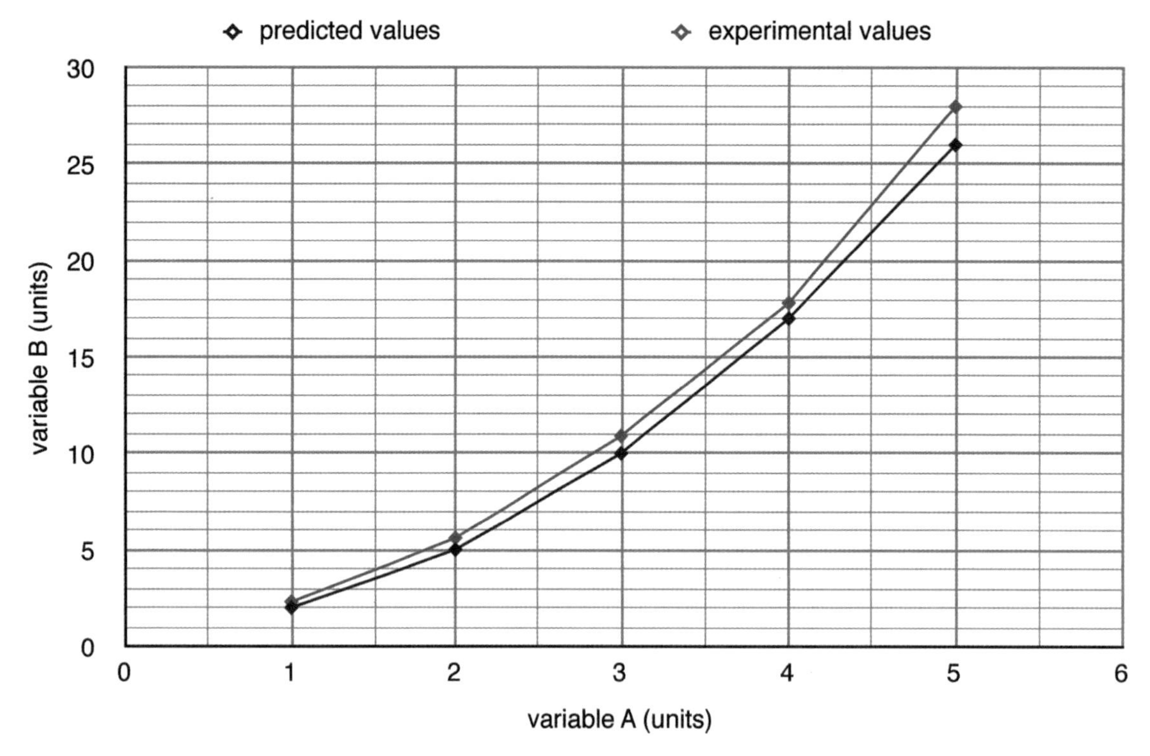

Figure 6-1. Predicted and experimental values for variable B vs. variable A.

Let's analyze the results for the example data set above. Graphical presentation of data is the best way to begin a qualitative analysis. In Figure 6-1, we should observe that the experimental curve has a very similar shape to the predicted curve. This means that the variation between the dependent and independent variables appears to match the prediction. In this case, the predicted values indicate that the dependent variable varies as the square of the dependent variable plus one. From the shape of the experimental curve, the variation in the experimental values appears to be the same. This type of agreement is an important confirmation of the scientific theory and should be noted in your analysis.

The quantitative analysis begins with the calculation of the percent difference. The calculation used for this is repeated once again here:

$$\text{percent difference} = \frac{|\text{predicted/accepted value} - \text{experimental value}|}{\text{predicted value}} \times 100\%$$

The percent difference must be calculated separately for each data point. Doing so for this example we obtain the values shown in Table 6-2.

Variable B, predicted (units)	Variable B, experimental (units)	Difference (%)
2.00	2.30	15.0
5.00	5.60	12.0
10.0	10.9	9.00
17.0	17.8	4.71
26.0	28.0	7.69

Table 6-2. Example values of the percent difference.

In the next section we will consider how to interpret percent difference figures such as these.

6.6 How Much Error is Too Much Error?

The magnitude of the percent difference that a scientist can consider acceptable for a successful experiment depends on many factors, including the quality of the equipment, the resolution of the measurement instruments, and the confidence the scientist has in the theoretical calculations. For example, the percent difference in experimental results related to a well-tested theory should be low, if the experiment involves accurate methods and high-quality measurement instruments. An experiment based on a new theory and new testing methods might produce a different result.

For high school science experiments conducted with standard high school grade equipment, achieving a result with a percent difference less than 5% is very good. Experiments with a difference this low can almost always be called a success. College science labs, commercial testing labs, and government research labs often have much more sophisticated equipment, and an acceptable percent difference might be much lower than 5%. In any lab, a percent difference in the 10-15% range would probably be regarded as mediocre, or maybe "not bad," and students should attempt to identify the most significant factors contributing to the difference, including errors of various kinds.

For lab exercises at the junior or senior level, the discussion should also address whether the factors the students identified could produce the amount of error observed. An example of this type of analysis was presented in Example 1 in Section 6.5. If the percent difference is higher than 15% or so, you should seriously address the question of what is wrong with the experiment to make the difference so large.

Returning to the percent difference calculation for the example data set on the previous page, we see that the difference values range from 4.7% to 15.0%. Given the good overall shape of the curve, we might judge these difference values to be "not bad." The percent difference is larger for small values of the variables, and the experimenter might explore why this is so, but overall this experiment can be viewed as successful. In conclusion, you should include in your report both qualitative and quantitative discussions of the percent difference, grounded in the graphs of the data and the percent difference calculations, respectively.

Finally, the percentage ranges I have discussed here are not clean boundaries. You should not quote these values in statements such as, "our errors were all below 5%, so that means our data are good." Instead of quoting 5%, 10%, or 15% as boundaries between "good" and "pretty good" and "not bad," simply use these values as guides for judging your own results and writing about them.

Chapter 7
Preparing Tables, Graphs, and Figures

7.1 Preliminaries

In the world of scientific publishing, there are well-known standards for formatting tables, graphs, and figures. Scientific journals everywhere tend to follow these same practices, so you need to learn them and follow them in your own lab reports.

Tables

Tables appear in almost every lab report. Use tables to report all your data and calculations. The requirements for placing, labeling, and titling tables are the same as those for graphs and figures discussed in Sections 3.4 and 7.2. Two specific standards apply to tables:

1. All data must be displayed with the correct number of significant digits. The significant digits in the data should match the significant digits you have recorded in your lab journal. These, in turn, should match the precision of the instrument you used to make your measurements. Calculated values should also be displayed with the correct number of significant digits.

2. Place the names of variables in the first row of the table and list the data in the column below the variable name. Be sure to show the units of measure for each variable, using the formatting and punctuation for units of measure presented in Section 7.2 (item 7).

Creating tables is easy to do in both Word and Pages by clicking the Tables icon. For this reason, we will not discuss the details of how to create tables in your word processor in this book.

Graphs

Graphs should be constructed, with great attention to the details covered later in this chapter, using an appropriate software application such as Excel on a PC, Excel on a Mac, Pages on a Mac, or Numbers on a Mac. Both Excel and Numbers can do anything you need to do, including formatting the graph for proper appearance. Pages can do almost everything, but it cannot construct a graph with proper uncertainty bars, which are unfortunately called "error bars" in all the applications. (There are "error bars" fields in Pages, they just don't work correctly. If you need uncertainty bars, build the graph in Numbers as explained in Section 7.5.) Graphs constructed by hand are not acceptable.

Just as with learning how to type papers in Word or Pages, setting up graphs in any of the applications listed in the previous paragraph involves a steep learning curve. Fortunately, these days software is getting pretty user friendly. Most of the rest of this chapter is devoted to detailed instructions for building graphs, which are called "charts" in all the applications. Look for the section titled with the computer and software version you are using. These sections are as follows:

Section	Computer	Software	Comments
7.4	PC	Office/Excel 2013	Current or latest version in wide use.
7.5	Mac	Pages 5.1/Numbers 3.1	Latest version.
7.6	PC	Office/Excel 2004	Included for those working with older software.
7.7	Mac	Pages '09 (version 4.3)	Included for those working with older software.
7.8	Mac	Office/Excel 2008 for Mac	Included for those working with older software.

Figures

Figures are diagrams, photos, or other graphics files. If you need to draw a diagram of your experimental setup, you can either do it on paper or with a graphics application of some kind. If you need to draw a figure by hand, do it neatly, use a straightedge, and scan the diagram so you can place it into your report file digitally. The old days of hand-drawn figures taped onto a page in the report are long gone, so don't do that. Fortunately, figures are not needed that often unless your setup cannot be described clearly without a diagram. Figures are also frequently used in biology labs, but these are generally photo images (possibly including labels and arrows) rather than diagrams.

7.2 Basic Formatting Requirements

1. All tables, graphs, and figures must be labeled and titled. We addressed this in detail in Section 3.4. Refer back to that section for the four rules that apply to labeling and titling these report elements.

2. When preparing a graph in an application such as Excel or Pages, the graph building tools allow you to setup a title box right in the graph. Instead of using this built-in title box, I prefer that students type the label and title in the word processor, just above or just below the pasted-in graph. Thus, my advice here is to not use the automatic graph titling feature when configuring the graph. If for whatever reason you do decide to use the title box when configuring the graph, then do not type the title in the word processor. In short, the title should not appear twice.

3. All tables, graphs, and figures must be referred to explicitly in the text in the numerical order in which they appear. (This also applies to all tables and figures.) No graph should be included unless you mention it explicitly somewhere in the narrative. Graphs are usually designated Graph 1, Graph 2, etc. As described previously, tables and figures are handled the same way.

4. In XY scatter plots (see Section 7.3), data points should always be shown. Whether the data points should be connected by a curve or not, and, if so, with what kind of curve (line segments or a fitted curve) will depend on the nature of the experiment and the data. Most of the time, you will show the data points and connect them with straight line segments. However, there are times in more advanced studies when smooth curve fitting is appropriate. If in doubt, ask your instructor which is best for the experiment you are working on.

5. As illustrated in the following sections, scales for graphs should be chosen appropriately to fit the data. The data should fit comfortably into the frame of the graph without crowding or unnecessary wasted space. When preparing the graph in Excel, the software will take care of this, but you need to make sure the automatic scales chosen by the application are suitable and change them if you need to.

6. Each of the axes on a graph must be labeled with a variable name and the corresponding units. There are two acceptable formats for the punctuation of axis labels. One format is to place a comma after the name of the variable followed by a space and the variable units. Examples of this format are as follows:

   volume, mL   mass, kg   velocity, m/s   temperature, °C

   The other standard format is to place a space after the variable name—without a comma—followed by the units in parentheses. Examples of this format are as follows:

   volume (mL)   mass (kg)   velocity (m/s)   temperature (°C)

   Note that the variable labels on the axes are not capitalized. Choose one of the two standard punctuation formats and use it consistently.

7. If multiple data sets or curves are represented on the same set of axes, a legend with different symbols to distinguish between the curves or data sets should be used and shown on the graph. The software automatically generates this legend. However, if there is only one curve on the graph, the legend is unnecessary and should be deleted. If you do use the legend because of multiple curves, you need to change the names of the data sets in the legend from Series 1, Series 2, etc. (the defaults), to meaningful names such as "experimental values" or "predicted values."

8. Regarding the use of curves or lines to connect the data points on a graph:

   a. This should only be done if interpolating between data points is meaningful. If interpolation has no meaning, data points should not be connected. For example, on a graph of gravitational potential energy (E_G) vs. height, interpolation is meaningful because the E_G of a height between two data points will be equal to the interpolated value. In contrast, in a chart showing the height of each student in a group, the height between two students is meaningless, and the data points should not be connected.

   b. If students know in advance that the data should follow a predicted curve (for example, a certain line or quadratic), the predicted curve should be shown on the graph so that the reader can see how well the data values correspond to the theoretical curve (see Example 2 in Chapter 9). If a *linear regression* is used to calculate the *line of best fit*, this line should be shown on the graph in most cases. This is discussed further in the next section.

7.3 Types of Graphs

Basic Graphs for All Students

The most common type of graph for science classes is called an *XY scatter plot*. An XY scatter plot is simply a graph of data values on a set of axes using Cartesian coordinates. As mentioned above, the data points on an XY scatter plot may be joined by line segments to form a curve. If the experimental data are to be compared to predicted values, then it is typical to show two curves on the same set of axes—one curve formed from the experimental data, the other formed from predicted values. In the following sections are example instructions for constructing graphs of XY scatter plots using PCs and Macs.

Advanced Graph Features—Trendlines and Uncertainty Bars

There are two advanced features common in graphs prepared by students in more advanced high school or college courses—the *trendline* and *uncertainty bars*. We will take the time to describe these here.

A trendline is the line representing a *mathematical regression* of a data set. The most common regression to use is the *linear regression*. An example graph of a data set with a linear trendline is shown in Figure 7-1. Instructions for adding a trendline to a graph are included at the end of Sections 7.4 (Excel 2013) and 7.5 (Pages 5.1). More advanced students will sometimes use other types of regressions besides the linear regression.

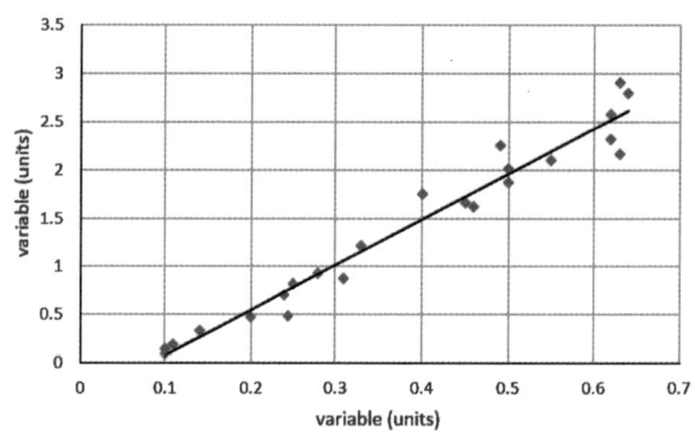

Figure 7-1. Example graph of data set with a linear regression trendline shown.

Uncertainty bars are used when you have data for multiple measurements (values of the dependent variable) for each value of the independent variable (the variable shown on the horizontal axis). On your graph, you typically show only the mean of the data for a given value of the independent variable. Then, as described in the Discussion section of Chapter 5 (Section 5.7), the uncertainty bars on the graph extend vertically above and below the mean value by a distance corresponding to the sample standard deviation, *s*, of the data represented by that mean value. An example graph of a data set showing uncertainty bars is shown in Figure 7-2.

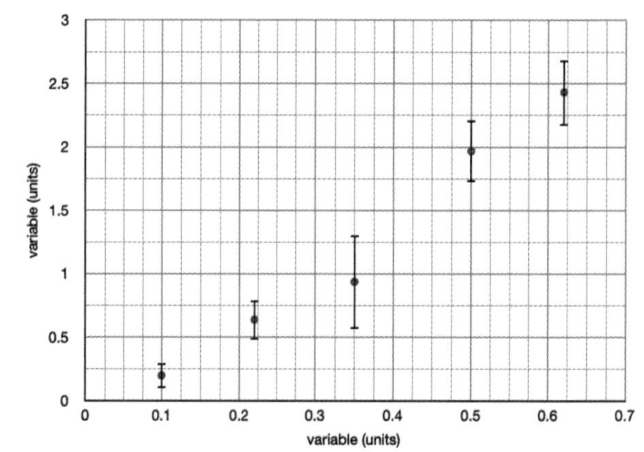

Figure 7-2. Example graph of data set with uncertainty bars shown.

For those working on PCs, graphs are always constructed in Microsoft Excel and then copied/pasted into your Word document. For PC users, instructions for adding uncertainty bars to graphs are at the end of Section 7.4.

For those working on Macs, most of the time graphs are constructed right in Pages without the use of a spreadsheet program. Trendlines can be added to graphs this way, but uncertainty bars cannot. As mentioned previously, the "error bar" feature in Pages does not work correctly unless you want all your error bars to be the same length. This may work for some applications, but I can't think of a use for it when working with scientific data. So Mac users, if you need to add uncertainty bars you will need to do what PC users do all the time: build your graph in a spreadsheet and then copy/paste the graph into Pages. On a Mac, the spreadsheet program is Numbers. Instructions for using Numbers to add uncertainty bars to graphs are at the end of Section 7.5.

7.4 Creating Graphs with Microsoft Excel on a PC (Office 2013)

Follow these steps to create an XY scatter plot in Microsoft Excel and paste it into a Word document.

Initial Setup

1. In Excel, list the values of the independent variable (horizontal axis) in order from least to greatest in column A and their corresponding values of the dependent variable (vertical axis) in column B.

   Note: If you are constructing two curves on the same graph (such as predicted and experimental curves), use column A for a single set of X-values. Then enter Y-values for the different data sets in columns B, C, etc. For example, enter the predicted values for each of your independent variable values in column B, and your experimental values in column C.

2. Select and highlight all X- and Y-values by clicking and dragging the mouse.

3. Click the INSERT tab of the main menu bar. In the Charts section, select the one that looks like a little graph with dots on it, the icon for an XY scatter plot. From the popup menu, select the XY scatter plot that has circles and dots connected together with straight lines. In general, always use a graph that displays the data points. Typically, you should choose the graph that connects the dots with straight lines. In some cases, your instructor may wish for you to use the one without any lines. For lower-level courses, you should probably stay away from the graphs that generate curved lines between data points. This automatic curve-fitting feature can generate some weird, confusing curves. The curve-fitting graphs are more appropriate for certain applications in upper-level classes.

After these initial steps, your graph should look like the one in Figure 7-3. Now we will go through the detailed configuration.

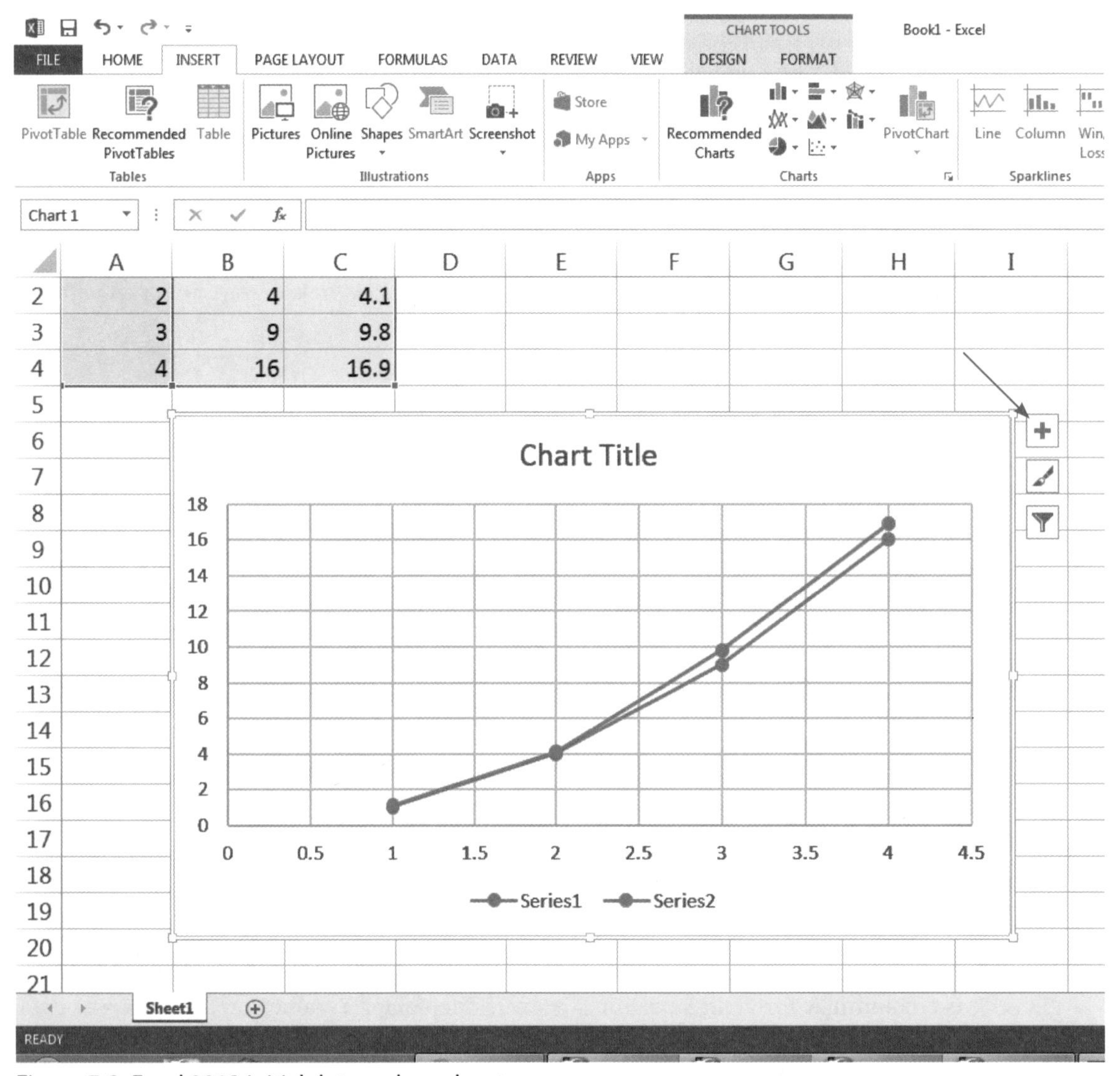

Figure 7-3. Excel 2013 initial data and graph set up.

Detailed Configuration

4. Click the Chart Elements icon that resembles a green plus sign at the upper right corner of your graph (indicated by a red arrow in Figure 7-3). In the popup menu, select Axes, Axis Titles, and Gridlines. If you have two or more curves to show on the graph, also select Legend. Deselect Chart Title.

5. Click on each of the axis titles, eliminate the default text, and type in the name of the variable with the units of measure using the standard formatting and punctuation for this, described in Section 7-2.

6. Click on the curve on the graph and select the FORMAT tab in the main menu at the top of the screen. A formatting panel will open up at the far right of the screen. Under SERIES OPTIONS, select the first one, which looks like a can of paint. Just below the Series Options icons, first select LINE. Reduce the default line width to 1 pt. Now under the SERIES OPTIONS icons, select MARKER and MARKER OPTIONS. Change the setting from Automatic to Built-in. Reduce the size from the default to 4. If you have two or more curves, repeat these actions for the other curves.

7. If you have a legend in your graph because you have two or more curves, do the following to change the default names to the specific descriptors ("predicted values," "experimental values," etc.) you want to have on your graph:

   a. Right-click on the legend. Click on Select Data.

   b. Click on one of the data series in the lower left portion of the panel. Then click the Edit table above the data series list.

   c. Type in your descriptor in the Series Name field in the popup menu.

8. Now we need to adjust the formatting of each of the axes. Do the following separately for each axis:

   a. Click on one of the scale values on one of the axes. The Formatting panel at the right, shown in Figure 7-4, will then say Format Axis. Click the fourth Axis Options icon called Axis Options that resembles three vertical bars. Under Axis Options, set the Bounds Maximum and Bounds Minimum to be the endpoints you want for the axis. These should be set to round numbers, and the maximum should be slightly larger than the highest value in the data set. In the example graph shown in Figure 7-3, the highest X-value is 4, so I set the Y-axis Bound Maximum to 5 instead of the 4.5 maximum that came up automatically. For the Y-axis, I changed the default 18 to 20, since 20 is also a bit more of a round number.

   b. While still under Axis Options, set the Units Major to the difference between values you want on the axis. Since my X-axis runs from 0 to 5, I set the Units Major field to 0.5. This places a gridline and scale value every 0.5 units. On the Y-axis, I set this value to 4.0.

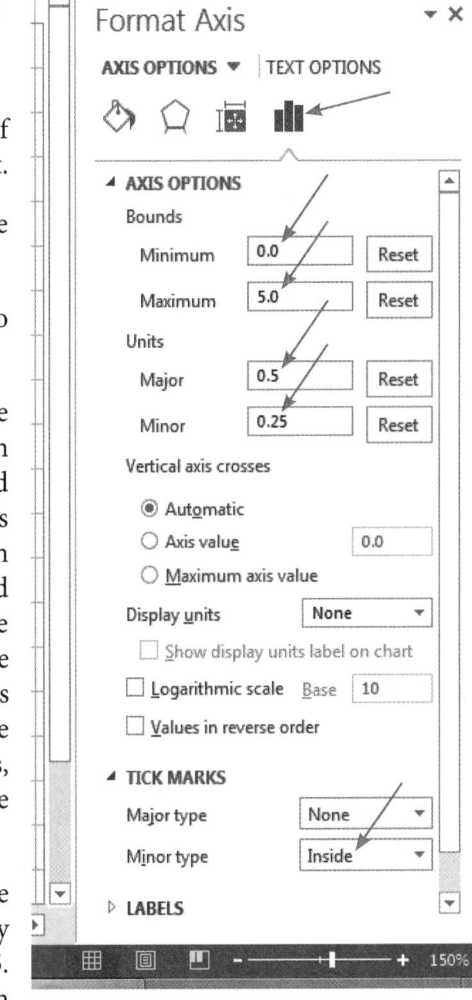

Figure 7-4. Excel 2013 axis settings in the Format Axis panel.

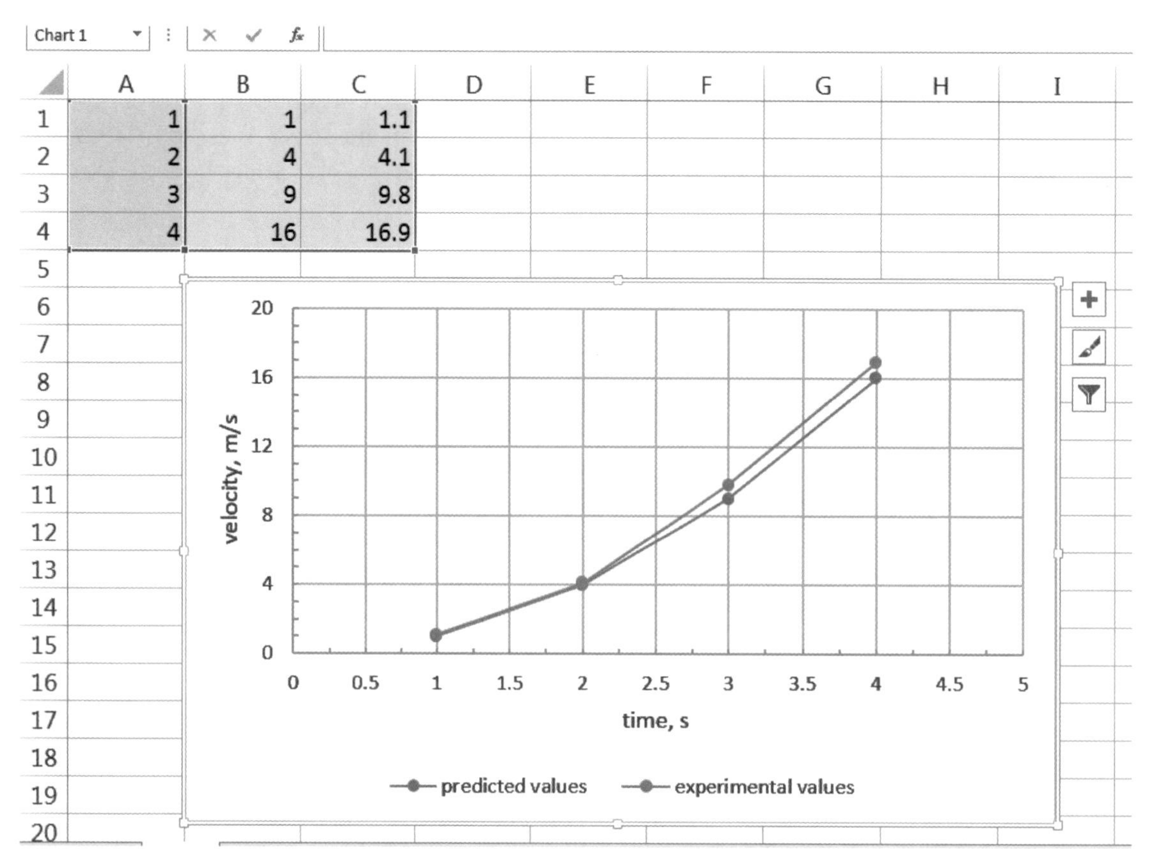

Figure 7-5. Excel 2013 completed graph.

Figure 1. Data plot of velocity vs. time.

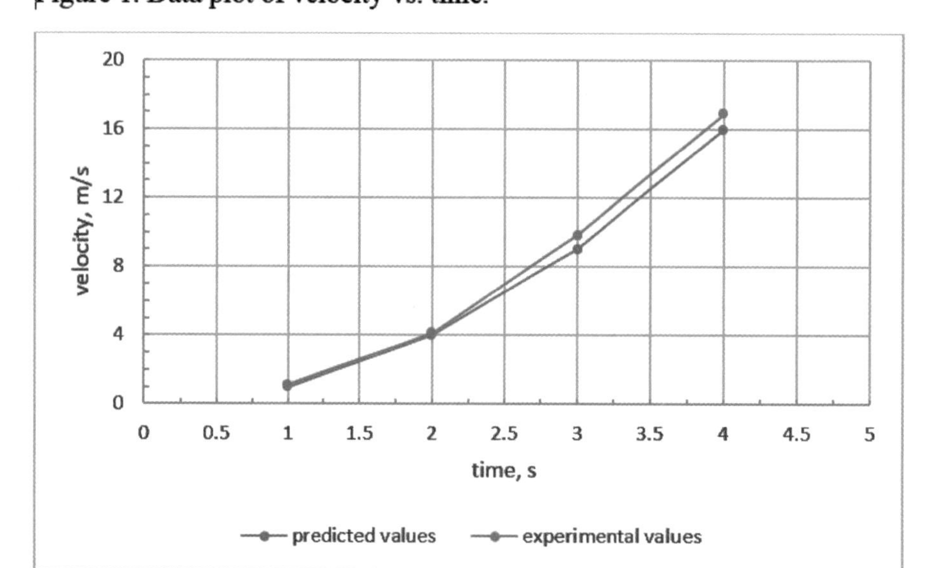

Figure 7-6. Excel 2013 completed graph pasted into Word with label and title.

c. It appears that in the 2013 version of Excel, the gridlines on the graph are fixed by the Units Major setting. This is unfortunate. I would prefer that we could configure the gridlines on the graph separately, as with previous versions of Excel. Since we can't turn on additional gridlines without making the scale on the axis look ridiculous, the only thing we can do is turn on the Tick Marks. So under the Axis Options panel, select Tick Marks. Set the Minor Type setting to Inside. Then configure how far apart you wish the tick marks to be by going back up to the Axis Options area and setting the Units Minor field.

At this point your graph is all there and should look similar to the example in Figure 7-5. You may have to click on the corner of the graph and stretch or shrink it to make it look right.

9. The graph is now ready to paste into the report. Click on the graph and copy it.

10. Switch over to Word where the report file is open. Place the cursor at the desired location for the graph and paste in the graph. You are done! You can click on the picture and place the cursor over the corner and click and drag to enlarge or shrink your picture to fit properly into the report. After you copy your graph and paste it into Word it should look similar to the graph in Figure 7-6. Notice in the figure that the label and title for the graph are typed in just above the graph.

Adding a Trendline (advanced courses)

11. After entering your data and configuring the graph as described above, click on the Chart Elements icon that looks like a green cross at the upper right of the graph. On the popup menu, select Trendline.

12. Click on the trendline in your graph. At the right of your screen, the Format Trendline panel will appear. At the top, select the paint can to format the trendline. Set the Color to black, the Dash Type to solid line, and the Width to 1 pt.

13. Normally, you will want to make sure Linear is selected, which is the choice when you wish to show the line resulting from a linear regression. (Students in upper-level classes may select the appropriate regression.) You can check the Display Equation on Chart field to see the equation

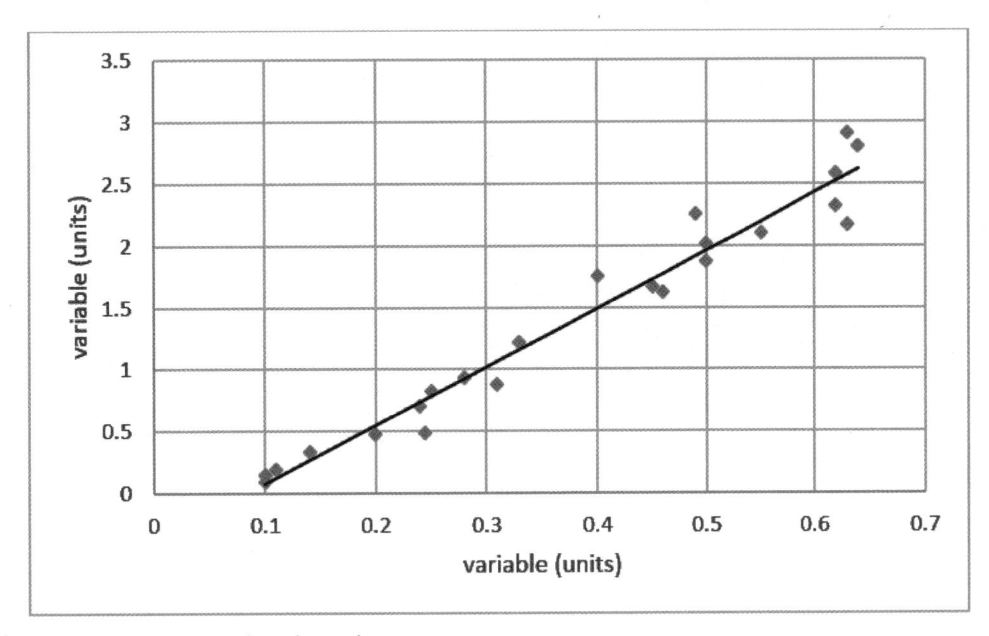

Figure 7-7. Excel 2013 completed graph.

for the trendline that will be shown on the graph (to see the slope or y-intercept). The equation shows up on the graph itself. Once you record the equation in your lab journal or report, you may or may not want it to be displayed on the graph.

14. The graph with the trendline should now appear as shown in Figure 7-7.

Adding Uncertainty Bars (upper-level courses)

15. First, put all of your data into the spread sheet by typing your X-values in column A, and the Y-values in column B. Skip a column or two and use two columns to enter each X-value one time, and next to it the mean for the Y-values corresponding to that X-value. With an operation as complex as this, it is a good practice to label your columns in Excel so that you can remember what they all mean. An example screen capture is shown in Figure 7-8. As you see, the complete set of data is listed in columns A and B. In columns E and F, I have listed each of the X-values and the corresponding mean of the Y-values. To setup and configure your graph, use the values in columns E and F. (Do not use the entire data set, only the single X-values and the means of the Y-values).

16. Now skip a column to the right of the Y-value means, and enter each of the Y-values that go with that mean, as shown in Figure 7-8 (Y1, Y2, etc.). I have five data points for each X-value. The five corresponding Y-values are listed in the same row in columns H through L.

The data are now all set up. Next we need to have the computer calculate the sample standard deviation of the Y-values for each of the X-values. Then we need to configure the uncertainty bars to use these standard deviation values to set the lengths of the bars.

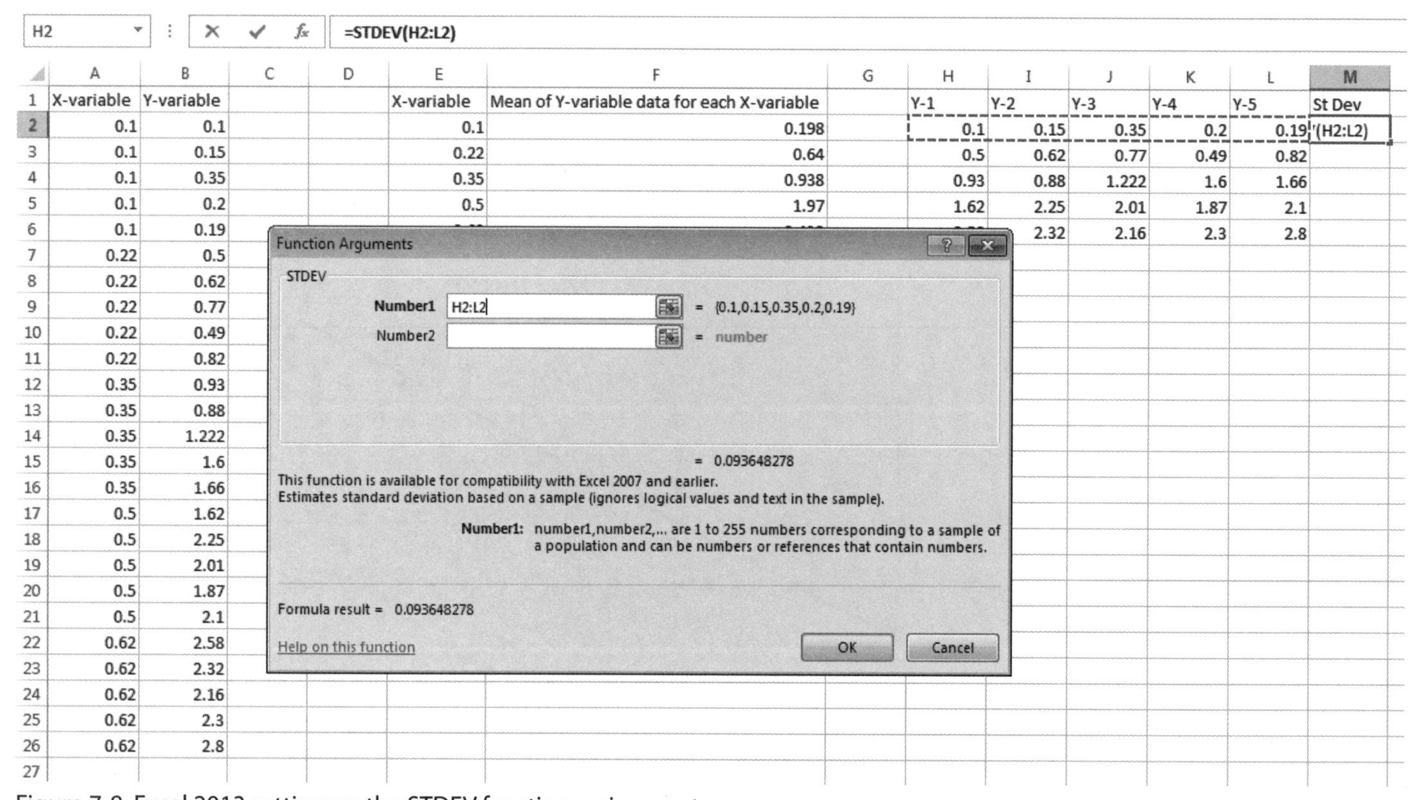

	A	B	C	D	E	F	G	H	I	J	K	L	M
1	X-variable	Y-variable			X-variable	Mean of Y-variable data for each X-variable		Y-1	Y-2	Y-3	Y-4	Y-5	St Dev
2	0.1	0.1			0.1	0.198		0.1	0.15	0.35	0.2	0.19	'(H2:L2)
3	0.1	0.15			0.22	0.64		0.5	0.62	0.77	0.49	0.82	
4	0.1	0.35			0.35	0.938		0.93	0.88	1.222	1.6	1.66	
5	0.1	0.2			0.5	1.97		1.62	2.25	2.01	1.87	2.1	
6	0.1	0.19							2.32	2.16	2.3	2.8	
7	0.22	0.5											
8	0.22	0.62											
9	0.22	0.77											
10	0.22	0.49											
11	0.22	0.82											
12	0.35	0.93											
13	0.35	0.88											
14	0.35	1.222											
15	0.35	1.6											
16	0.35	1.66											
17	0.5	1.62											
18	0.5	2.25											
19	0.5	2.01											
20	0.5	1.87											
21	0.5	2.1											
22	0.62	2.58											
23	0.62	2.32											
24	0.62	2.16											
25	0.62	2.3											
26	0.62	2.8											
27													

Figure 7-8. Excel 2013 setting up the STDEV function assignment.

17. Click the top cell in the next column to the right of your Y-value data (cell M2 in Figure 7-8). In this column we need to put the sample standard deviations for each row of data. To do this, first click on the function icon, f_x, in the toolbar. (This is also available in the Formulas menu under Insert Function.) In the drop down menu, scroll down to STDEV, the sample standard deviation. Select this function and click OK. The Function Arguments dialog box will open, but you don't need to enter anything into this box directly. As shown in the figure, if your STDEV column is right next to the data used to compute the standard deviation, Excel should automatically enter a code identifying the cells that will be included in the standard deviation calculation. In the figure, the first set of Y-values is in cells H2 through L2. The code Excel uses for this, H2:L2, is shown in the Function Arguments dialog box, and in the STDEV cell (M2) in the spreadsheet as (H2:L2). If the correct set of cells does not automatically appear, then do this: While the dialog box is still open, click the first Y-value cell and drag to include all the Y-value cells for the first X-value as indicated by the dashed rectangle in Figure 7-8. The sample standard deviation for the first row of data now appears in the cell (M2 in our example). Click OK in the dialog box.

18. To get the standard deviation values to appear for the other rows of data, select the first standard deviation value, then click on the lower right corner of that cell (where the tiny black square is) and drag it down to include all the cells in the column. In Figure 7-9, the cells are M2 through M6.

19. Click on your graph, and on the Chart Elements icon that looks like a green cross at the upper right of the graph, select Error Bars. Both horizontal and vertical uncertainty bars will appear on your graph. Click on one of the horizontal bars and hit delete. This should leave only vertical uncertainty bars at each data point.

20. Click on one of the vertical uncertainty bars and the Format Error Bars panel will open at the right of your screen. At the top under Error Bar Options, select the third icon, which looks like three vertical bars. In the Vertical Error Bar panel below, select the following:

    a. Direction: Both
    b. End Style: Cap
    c. Error Amount: Custom

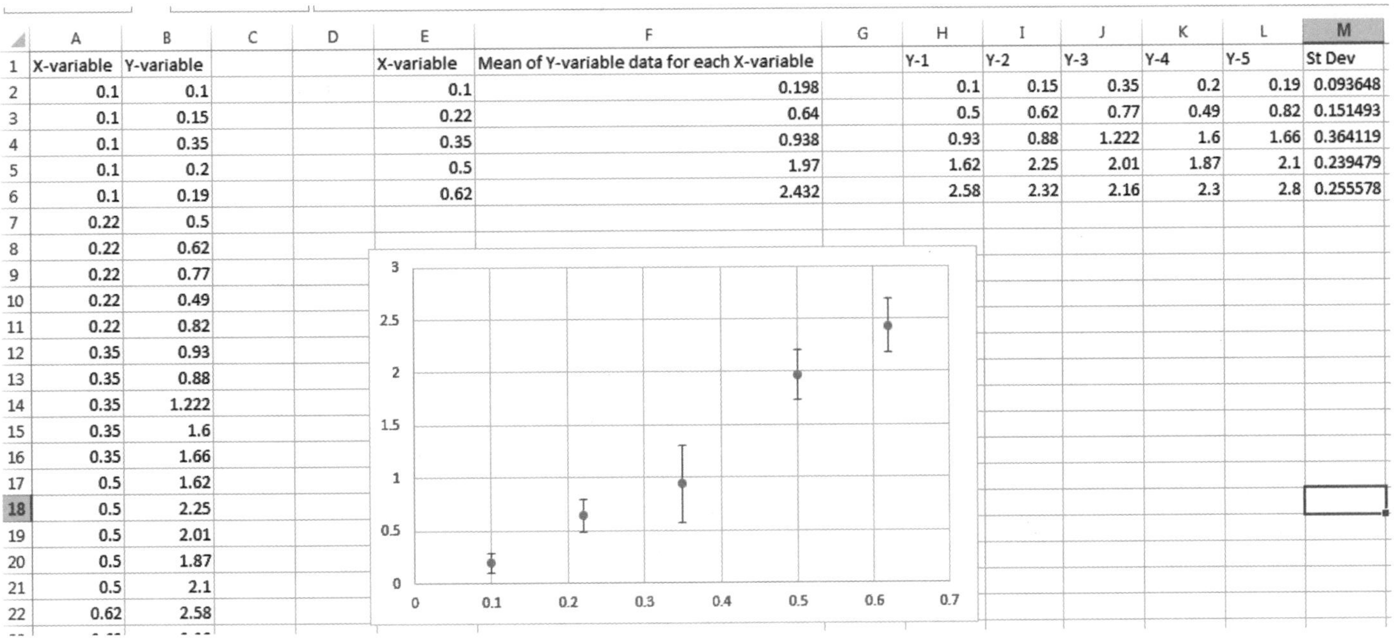

	A	B	C	D	E	F	G	H	I	J	K	L	M
1	X-variable	Y-variable			X-variable	Mean of Y-variable data for each X-variable		Y-1	Y-2	Y-3	Y-4	Y-5	St Dev
2	0.1	0.1			0.1	0.198		0.1	0.15	0.35	0.2	0.19	0.093648
3	0.1	0.15			0.22	0.64		0.5	0.62	0.77	0.49	0.82	0.151493
4	0.1	0.35			0.35	0.938		0.93	0.88	1.222	1.6	1.66	0.364119
5	0.1	0.2			0.5	1.97		1.62	2.25	2.01	1.87	2.1	0.239479
6	0.1	0.19			0.62	2.432		2.58	2.32	2.16	2.3	2.8	0.255578
7	0.22	0.5											
8	0.22	0.62											
9	0.22	0.77											
10	0.22	0.49											
11	0.22	0.82											
12	0.35	0.93											
13	0.35	0.88											
14	0.35	1.222											
15	0.35	1.6											
16	0.35	1.66											
17	0.5	1.62											
18	0.5	2.25											
19	0.5	2.01											
20	0.5	1.87											
21	0.5	2.1											
22	0.62	2.58											

Figure 7-9. Excel 2013 setting up the uncertainty bars.

21. Then click on the Specify Value Box and the Custom Error Bars dialog box opens. Click in the Positive Error Value field and delete the contents. Leave your blinking cursor in that field and use the mouse to select all of the standard deviation values in the spreadsheet. In Figure 7-9, this would be cells M2 through M6. Now do a paste (ctrl-v) to enter all this information into the Positive Error Value field in the Specify Value box. For the Negative Error Value field, repeat this action using the same standard deviation values.

22. After closing the Custom Error Bars box by pressing OK, your graph will have the uncertainty bars for $\pm 1s$ as they appear in the graph in Figure 7-9. At a given X-value, the bar extends above and below the mean by a length equal to the sample standard deviation for the data at that X-value.

7.5 Creating Graphs with Pages on a Mac (Pages 5.1 and Numbers 3.1)

If you use Pages on a Mac to write your lab reports, you can prepare your graphs in Pages with the built-in Charts tool. The following instructions address how to configure an XY scatter plot, including the option of showing more than one curve on the same set of axes and a trendline

To Start

1. In Pages, place your cursor in the document where you want the graph to appear. Click on the *Chart* icon at the top of the page and click the choice that looks like data points (+) on a graph. You enter your data by clicking the blue Enter Chart Data button to open the Chart Data Editor. Nearly everything else is configured in the panel to the right of your document.

Entering Data in the Chart Data Editor

2. If the Chart Data Editor has any default or sample data in it when you open it, delete the data values. In the X column, enter your values for the independent variable (X-values). If you are plotting a single curve on the graph, enter the values for the dependent variable (Y-values) in the first of the Y columns. If you wish to construct more than one curve on the graph, enter the Y-values for the other curves in the additional Y columns.

3. If you have two or more curves to plot on the same graph, the headers just below the colored bars in the Chart Data Editor are a place where you can label the data columns with the labels you want to appear in the legend for the different curves on the graph. (You can also edit these labels right in the legend that appears above the graph.)

Configuring the Graph

The following settings are made in the graph configuration panel on the right side of your Pages document. At the top of the panel are the general menu tabs *Chart*, *Axis*, *Series*, and *Arrange*.

4. If you only have one curve on your graph, you should not show the legend. To turn the legend off, click on the *Chart* tab in the configuration panel and uncheck the *Legend* selection.

5. Under the *Axis* tab, do the following for both the X-axis and the Y-axis:

    a. Under Axis Options, select both Axis Name and Axis Line.

       Over on your graph, for each axis, click on the title field, then click again to place the cursor inside the box. Type the name of the appropriate variable, including the units of measure, according to the formatting requirements discussed in Section 7.2.

b. In the Major Gridlines and Minor Gridlines field, turn on the gridlines by selecting the solid line type. Set the point size for the Major Gridlines at 0.5 pt, and for the Minor Gridlines at 0.25 pt.

c. Set the following for each axis, as shown in Figure 7-10:

i. Appropriate minimum and maximum values to cover the range of your data.

To give your graph the correct proportions, always set the scale maximum values at a *round number* that is *slightly larger* than your largest data value. Figure 7-10 shows the highest Y-value in my example graph to be 16.9, and thus the Max setting for the Y-axis is set at 20.

ii. Use the *Steps Major* and *Minor* fields to set the number of gridlines you want for the axis.

You should show an appropriate number of gridlines to make it easy to estimate the values of your data points. Referring to Figure 7-11, the Max X-value is 5 with 5 major steps. This means each step will be worth one unit. I set the Minor field to four. This places four lines between each major gridline, resulting in five spaces between each major gridline. This means the minor lines on the X-axis are spaced 0.2 units apart. You can see in Figure 7-11 that this produces a good looking graph, and it is easy to estimate data values from the axis scale.

6. Under the *Series* tab, do the following:

a. Under Data Symbols, select the symbol you wish to use for your data points. Then reduce the default size from 10 to 6.

b. Under Connection Lines, select Straight, the usual setting for an XY scatter plot.

7. Your completed graph should now appear as shown in Figure 7-12. You can click on the graph and drag it to where you want it. Position the little blue margin symbol right at the end of the label and title for your graph, with the graph just below, as shown in Figure 7-13.

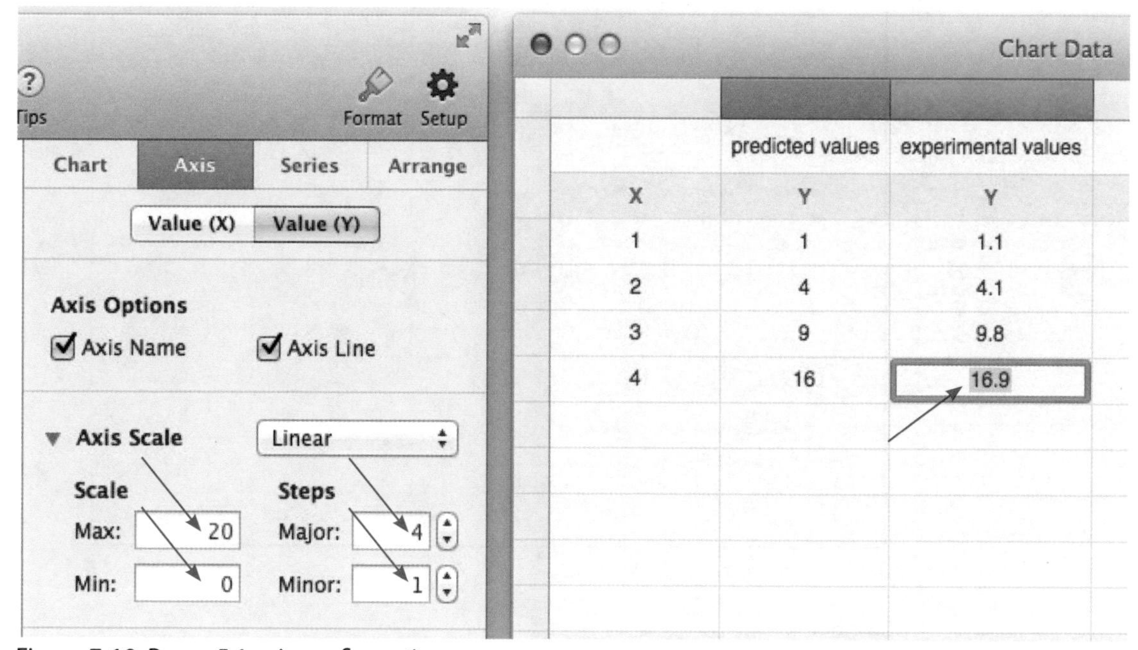

Figure 7-10. Pages 5.1 axis configuration.

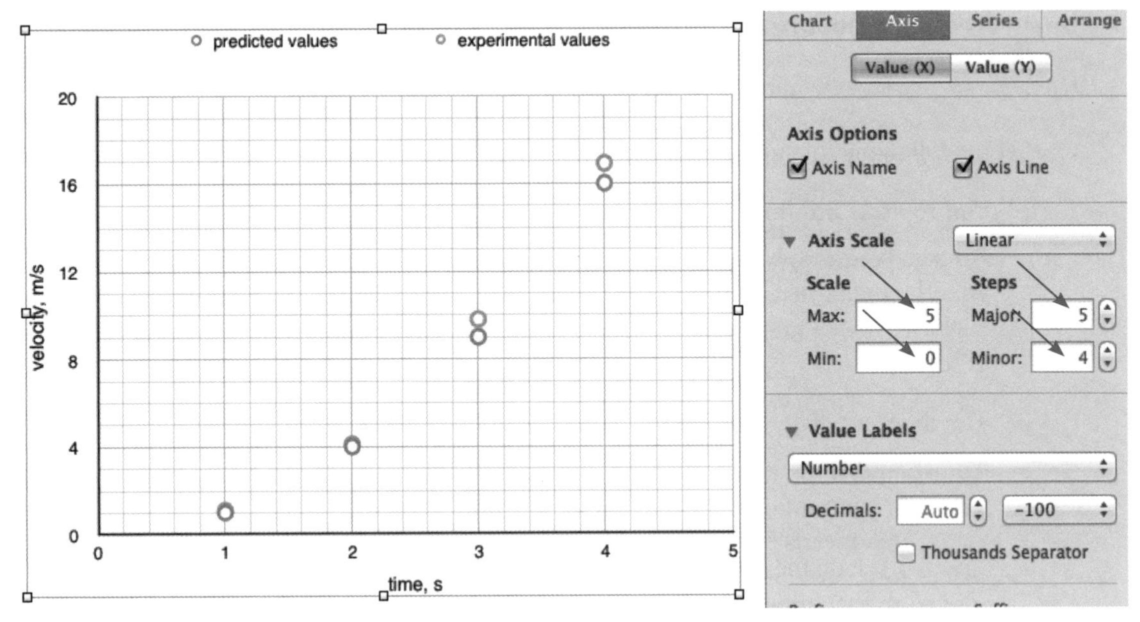

Figure 7-11. Pages 5.1 gridline configuration.

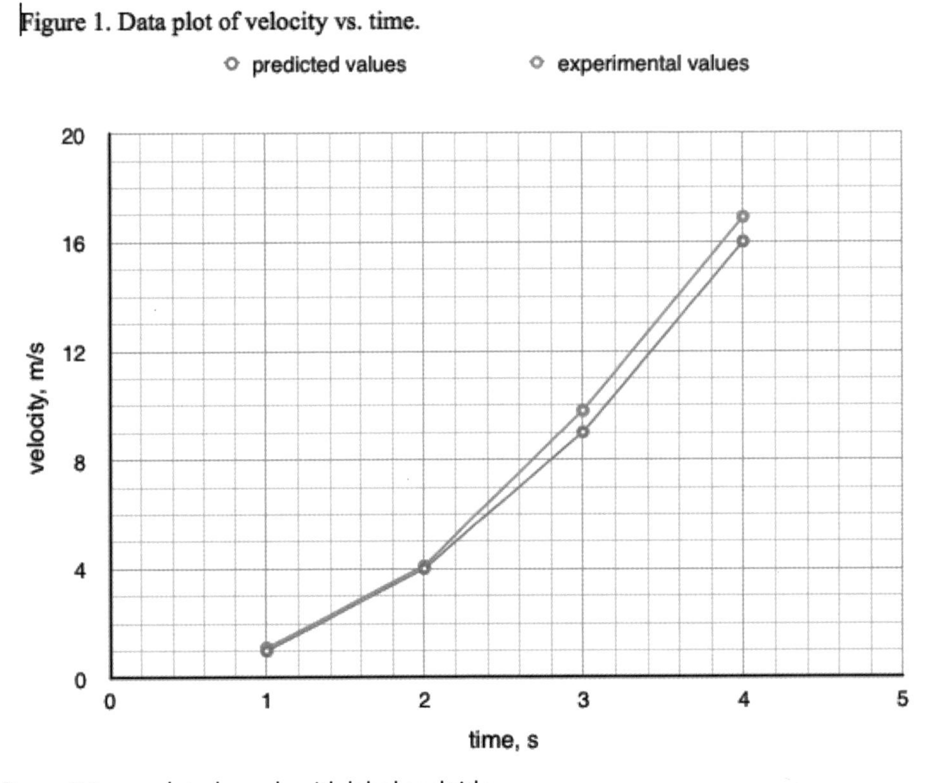

Figure 7-12. Pages 5.1 completed graph with label and title.

Adding a Trendline (advanced courses)

8. To add a trendline for a data set to a graph, select the Series tab. Under Trendlines, select Linear for a straight trendline, which is the choice when you wish to show the line resulting from a linear regression. (Students in upper-level classes may select the appropriate regression.) You can check the Show Equation field to see the equation for the trendline that will be shown on the graph (to see the slope or y-intercept). The equation shows up on the graph itself. Once you record the equation in your lab journal or report, you may or may not want it to be displayed on the graph.

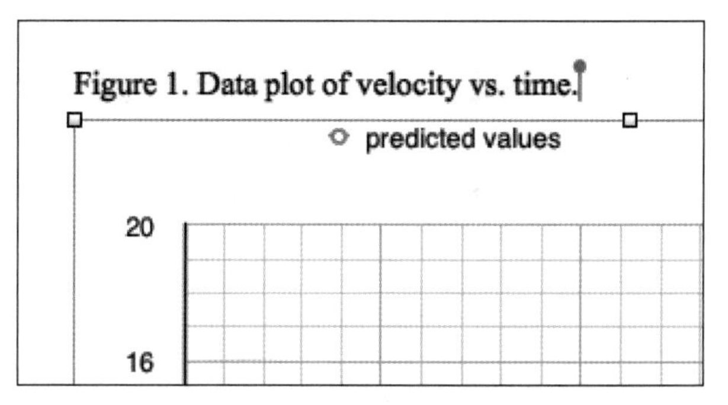

Figure 7-13. Pages 5.1 graph positioning in the report document.

9. Once the line is present, you need to adjust its appearance. Click on the line and select the Trendline tab that appears at the top of the configuration panel. Change the stroke color to black and the size to 1 pt. Then uncheck the Shadow box. A graph with a linear regression trendline is shown in Figure 7-14.

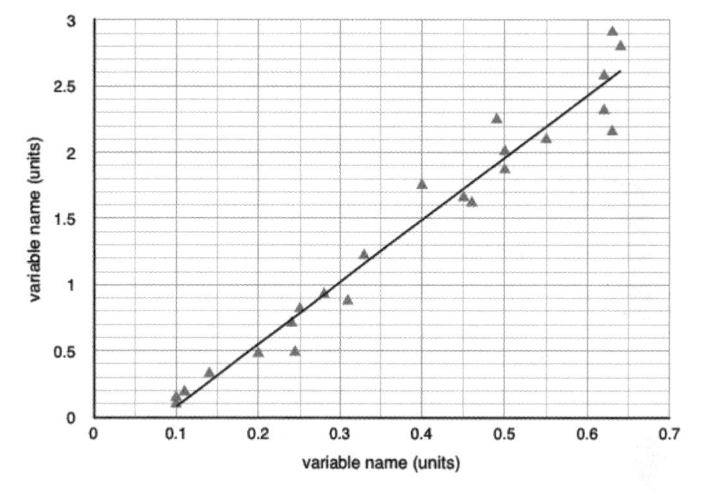

Figure 7-14. Pages 5.1 scatter plot with trendline.

Adding Uncertainty Bars (upper-level courses)

As a Mac user, you are probably used to setting up your graphs in Pages right where you prepare your report. However, as mentioned in Section 7.3, the "error bar" feature in Pages does not work correctly. So Mac users, if you need to add uncertainty bars you will need to build your graph in a spreadsheet and then copy/paste the graph into Pages. On a Mac, the spreadsheet program is Numbers. The instructions below pertain to Numbers 3.1.

10. First, put all of your data into the spreadsheet by typing your X-values in the first column and the Y-values in the second column. Skip a column or two and use two columns to enter each X-value one time, and next to it the mean for the Y-values corresponding to that X-value. With an operation as complex as this, it is a good practice to label your columns in Numbers so that you can remember what they all mean. An example screen capture is shown in Figure 7-15. As you see, the complete set of data is listed in columns B and C. In columns E and F, I listed each of the X-values and the corresponding mean of the Y-values. To setup and configure your graph, use the values in columns E and F. (Do not use the entire data set, only the single X-values and the means of the Y-values).

11. Now skip a column to the right of the Y-value means and enter each of the Y-values that go with that mean, as shown in Figure 7-15 (Y-1, Y-2, etc.). I have five data points for each X-value. The five corresponding Y-values are listed in the same row in columns H through L.

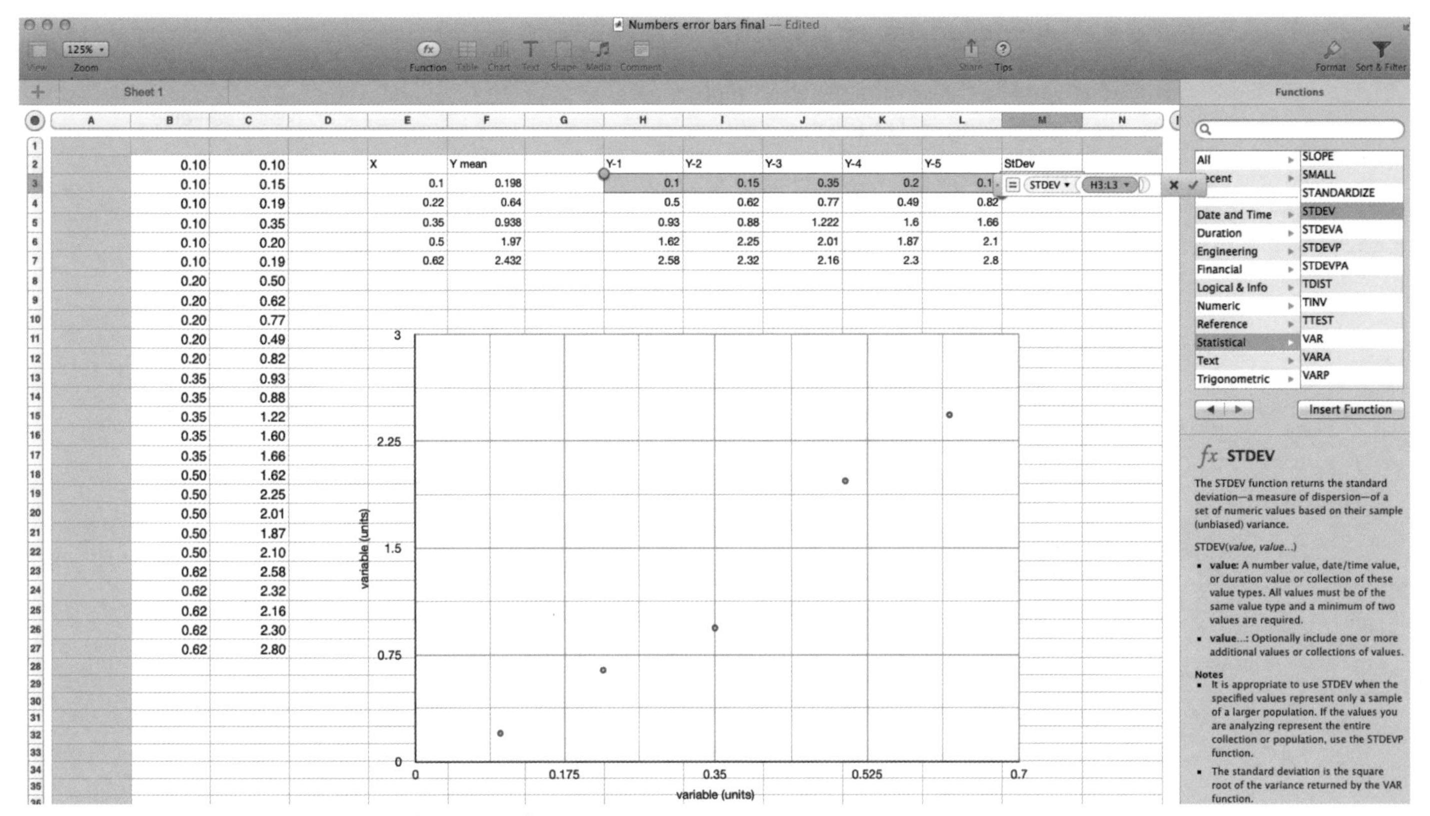

Figure 7-15. Numbers 3.1 setting up the STDEV function assignment.

The data are now all set up. Next we need to have the computer calculate the sample standard deviation of the Y-values for each of the X-values. Then we need to configure the uncertainty bars to use these standard deviation values to set the lengths of the bars.

12. In the column next to your Y-values, we need to put the sample standard deviations for each row of data. To do this, first click on the cell to the right of the first row of Y-values (cell M3 in Figure 7-15). Next, click on the function icon, f_x, in the toolbar above and select Create Formula. This causes the Functions panel to open up at the right side of the screen. In the selection field of the Functions panel, select Statistical on the left and scroll down the right side to STDEV, the sample standard deviation. Select this function and click Insert Function. Next, click on the first of the Y-values in that row and drag the cursor to select all of the Y-values in that row, as shown in Figure 7-15. Then click the green check mark at the right of the cell where the STDEV value is being placed. The standard deviation for the Y-values on that row should now appear in that cell (cell M3 in Figure 7-15).

13. Repeat the previous step for each row of Y-values.

Now we have the standard deviations. The last steps are to activate and configure the uncertainty bars.

14. As illustrated in Figure 7-16, click on your graph and select the Series tab at the top of the configuration panel. At the bottom of the panel, leave the X Axis Error Bars set to None. Change the Y Axis Error Bars setting to Positive and Negative. In the Use field that opens up, select Custom Values. Place your cursor in the Positive: field, then click and drag to select all of the standard deviation values created in the previous steps. Then click the green check mark to accept the entries. Repeat this for the Negative: field. These two fields should appear as they are in Figure 7-16, and you should see the uncertainty bars on your graph.

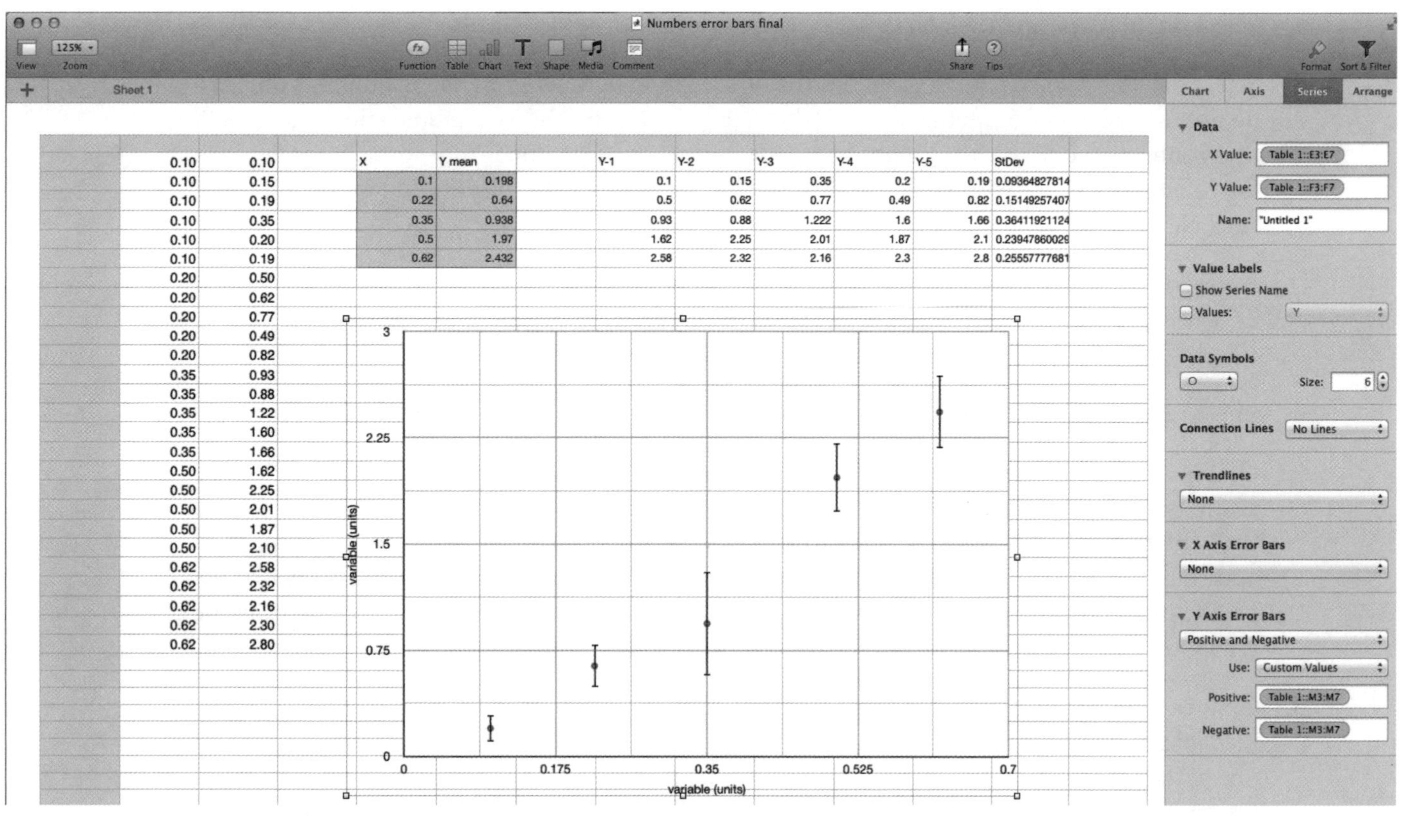

Figure 7-16. Numbers 3.1 setting up the error bars.

15. The final step is to make sure the uncertainty bars have the correct appearance. Click on one of the bars in your graph. Then select the Error Bars tab at the top of the configuration panel. Set the parameters to be a solid line with weight of 1 pt. The correct button for the appearance of the bar is the one on the right that looks like a line segment with short perpendicular line segments at each end.

16. Your graph should now have the uncertainty bars for $\pm 1s$ as they appear in the graph in Figure 7-16. At a given X-value, the bars extend above and below the mean by a length equal to the sample standard deviation for the data at that X-value.

7.6 Creating Graphs with Microsoft Excel on a PC (Office 2004)

Follow these steps to create an XY scatter plot in Microsoft Excel (Office 2004) and paste it into a Word document.

1. In Excel, list the values of the independent variable (horizontal axis) in order from least to greatest in column A and their corresponding values of the dependent variable (vertical axis) in column B.

   Note: If you are constructing two curves on the same graph (such as predicted and experimental curves), use column A for a single set of X-values. Then enter Y-values for the different data sets in columns B, C, etc. For example, enter the predicted values for each of your independent variable values in column B and your experimental values in column C.

2. Select and highlight all of these values by clicking and dragging the mouse.

3. Click on the Chart Wizard icon, which looks like a little bar chart.

4. Select XY (Scatter) and click Next.

5. Select the appropriate type of graph. Three of the graph options show the data points and two do not. Always use a graph that displays the data points. Typically, you should choose the graph that connects the dots with straight lines (the bottom left selection). Your instructor may wish for you to use the one without any lines. Click on the picture with the desired type of graph and click Next.

   Note: For lower level courses you should probably stay away from the graphs that generate curved lines between data points. This automatic curve-fitting feature can generate some weird, confusing curves. The curve-fitting graphs are more appropriate for certain applications in upper-level classes.

6. In step 2 of the Chart Wizard, select "Columns" from the Data Range tab. Then click Next.

7. On the Chart Options page, type in the variable names and units of measure for each of the axes, again using the standard formatting described in Section 7.2. My preference is that you not use the field for the Graph Title. As I mentioned in Section 7.2, I prefer that students type the label and title in the word processor (not in the graph configuration), just above or just below the pasted-in graph. If for whatever reason you do decide to use the title box when configuring the graph, then do not type the title in the word processor. The title should not appear twice.

8. On the Gridlines tab of this same page, select the gridlines options that make the graph most easily readable. Major gridlines for both X and Y axes will be needed, and possibly minor gridlines for one or the other or both. The screen capture shown in Figure 7-17 has Major and Minor gridlines for the X-axis and Major gridlines for the Y-axis. After selecting the gridlines, click Next.

9. On step 4 of the wizard verify that the chart will be an object in sheet 1, then click Finish.

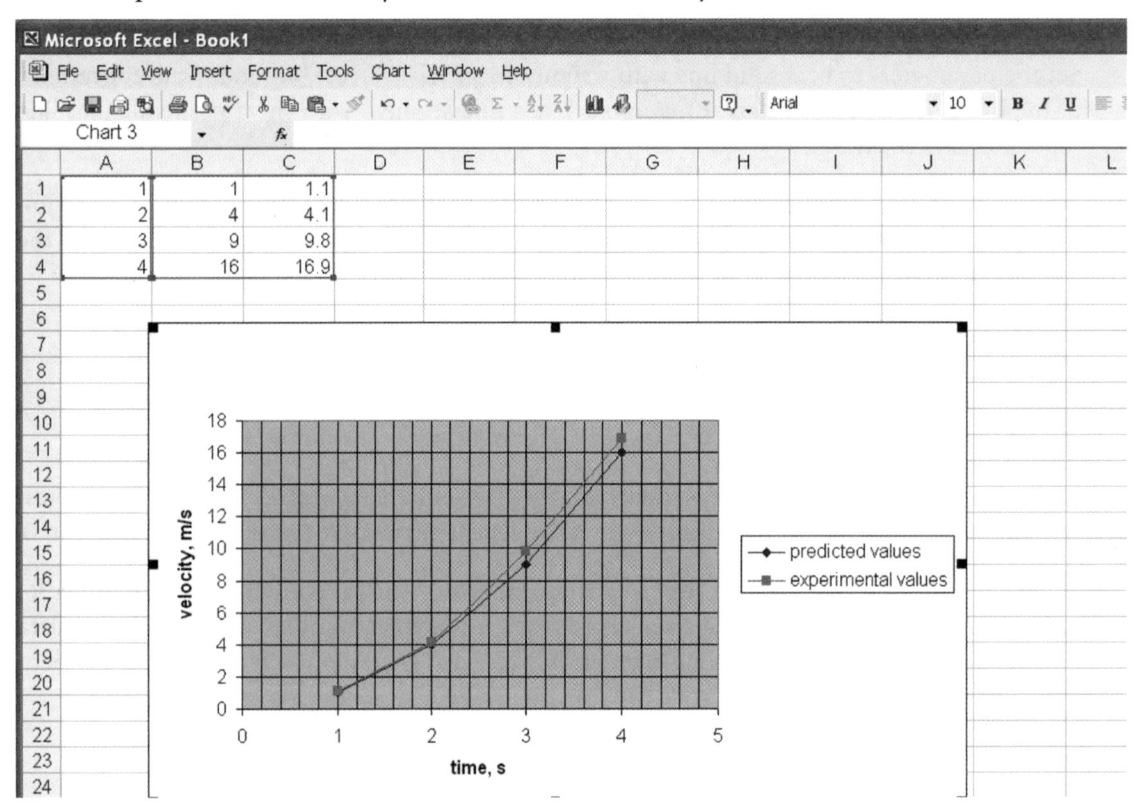

Figure 7-17. Excel 2004 initial data and graph set up.

10. If you have only one curve on the graph, you have a legend off to the right that says, "Series 1." This legend shouldn't be there with only one curve, so click on it and hit Delete. If you have two or more curves on the graph, the legend is necessary and you need to change the titles in the legend to describe what the curves actually represent. To do this, right click on the graph in the white border area and select Source Data from the popup menu. Under the Series tab, click on Series 1 under Series on the left and type in the name for Series 1 in the Name field on the right. Then click on Series 2 and type in the name for Series 2.

At this point your graph is all there and should look similar to the example in Figure 7-17. You may have to click on the corner of the graph and stretch or shrink it to make it look right. However, we aren't quite done. The defaults for the shading in the chart area and the fonts in the titles are too flashy for a scientific work and need to be toned down.

11. Place the cursor in the gray Plot Area of the graph and right-hand click. Select Format Plot Area from the pop-up menu. On the right side of the pop up under Area, select None for the color of the plot area and click OK.

12. The default font sizes for the axis titles are fine (10 point) but we need to remove the default bold print Excel uses for the titles. One at a time, double click on each of the axis titles. On the Font tab of the popup menu, select Regular under Font Style and click Okay. Your graph should now look like the graph shown in Figure 7-18.

13. The graph is now ready to paste into the report. Place the cursor inside the graph but near the edge and right click. Select Copy from the menu.

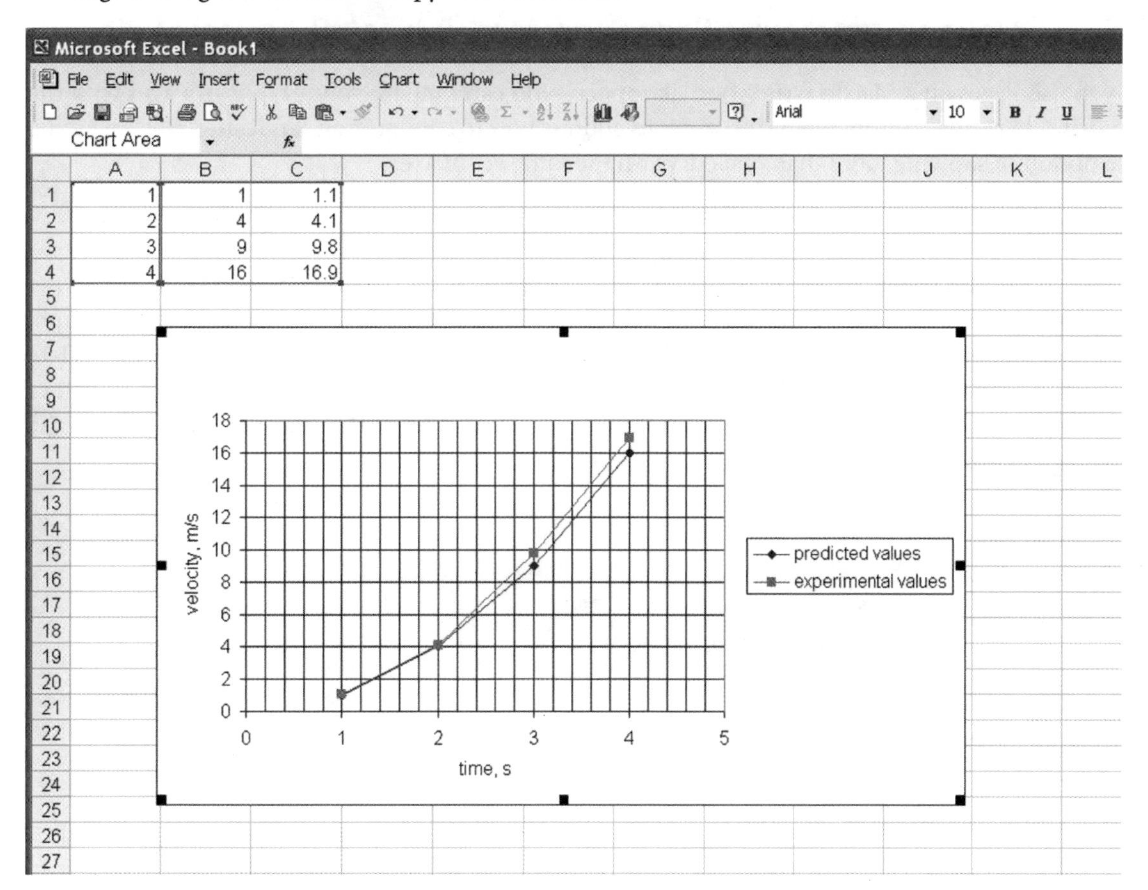

Figure 7-18. Excel 2004 completed graph.

Graph 1. Data plot of velocity vs. time.

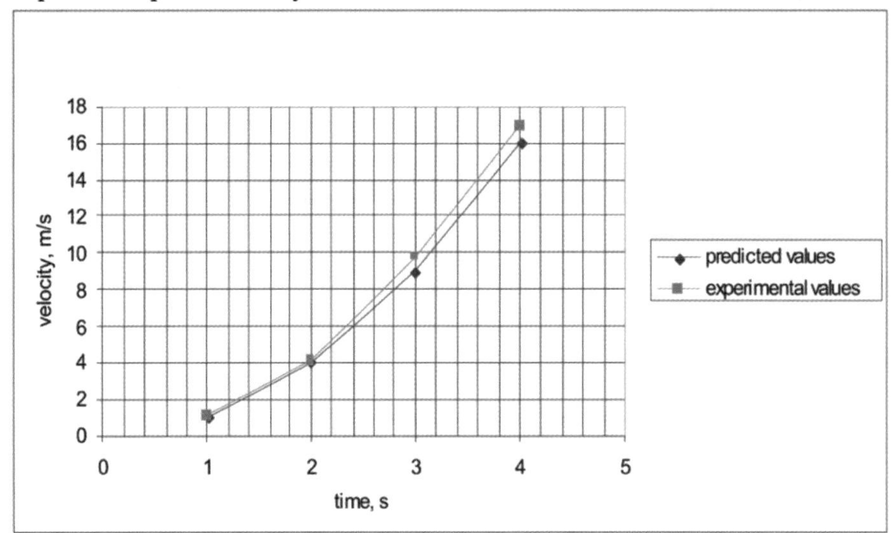

Figure 7-19. Excel 2004 finished graph after pasting into Word with label and title.

14. Switch over to Word where the report file is open. Place the cursor at the desired location for the graph and right click. Select Paste from the menu. You are done! You can click on the picture and place the cursor over the corner and click and drag to enlarge or shrink your picture to fit properly into the report. After you copy your graph and paste it into Word, it should look like Figure 7-19.

7.7 Creating Graphs with Pages on a Mac (Pages '09, version 4.3)

If you use Pages on a Mac to write your lab reports, you can prepare your graphs in Pages with the built-in Charts tool. The following instructions address how to configure an XY Scatter Plot, including the option of showing more than one curve on the same set of axes.

To Start

1. In Pages, place your cursor in the document where you want the graph to appear. Click on the Charts icon at the top of the page and click the choice that looks like data points on a graph. Two tool panels will open up: the Inspector, with the charts icon selected, and the Chart Data Editor. You enter your data in the Chart Data Editor, shown in Figure 7-20 with the data values for the example graph we will build in this section. Nearly everything else is configured in the Inspector panel.

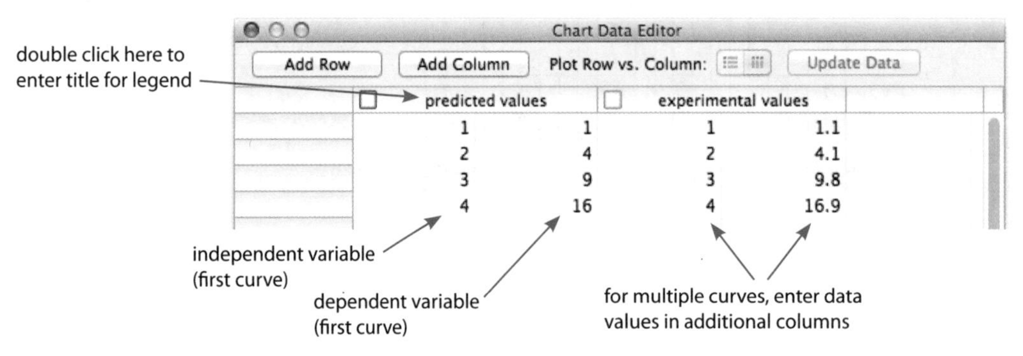

Figure 7-20. Pages '09 entering data in the Chart Data Editor.

Entering Data in the Chart Data Editor

2. If the Chart Data Editor has any default or sample data in it when you open it, delete the data values. At the tops of the columns, there are headers with colored squares next to them. Under each of the headers is a pair of columns for the data values for one curve. Under each header, you enter the values for the independent variable (horizontal axis) in the left column and the dependent variable (vertical axis) in the right column. For each curve on your graph, you need one header with a pair of columns below. If there are other unneeded headers in the Chart Data Editor, just click on the unwanted header and delete it.

3. If you have two or more curves to plot on the same graph, the headers in the Chart Data Editor are a place where you can label the data columns with the labels you want to appear in the legend for the different curves on the graph. (You can also edit these labels right in the legend that appears above the graph.) If you only have one curve on your graph, you should not show the legend. To turn the legend off, click on the Chart tab in the upper portion of the Inspector panel and uncheck the Legend field.

Settings in the Inspector Panel

4. Under the Axis tab in the Inspector panel, do the following:

   a. Use the Choose Axis Options menu to turn on the features you need on the graph, as shown in Figure 7-21. For typical XY scatter plots, you will need to activate the following selections:

      Show Axis
      Show Title
      Show Value Labels
      Show Minimum Value
      Linear Scale
      No Tick Marks
      Show Major Gridlines
      Show Minor Gridlines

      Close the Chart Axis Options by clicking again on the Chart Axis Options bar.

   b. For each axis, click on the title field, then click again to place the cursor inside the box. Type the name of the appropriate variable, including the units of measure, according to the formatting requirements discussed in Section 7.2.

   c. Set the following for each axis, as shown in Figure 7-22:

      i. Appropriate minimum and maximum values to cover the range of your data.

         To give your graph the correct proportions, always set the scale maximum values at a *round number* that is *slightly larger* than your largest data value. Figure 7-20 shows the highest Y-value in my example graph to be 16.9, and thus the Max setting for the Y-axis in Figure 7-22 is set at 20.

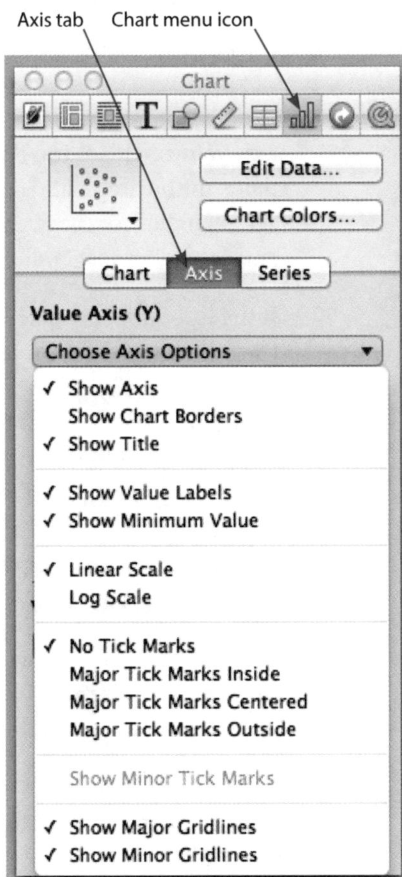

Figure 7-21. Pages '09 setting axis options in the Inspector panel.

ii. Use the Steps and Minor fields to set the number of gridlines you want for the axis.

You should show an appropriate number of gridlines to make it easy to estimate the values of your data points. In the example of Figure 7-22, the Max Y-value is 20 with 5 major steps. This means each step will be worth four units. By setting the Minor field to three, three minor gridlines are placed between each major gridline and the lines are spaced one unit apart.

5. Do the following separately for each curve on your graph. Click on one of the data points on the curve in your graph, then use the Series tab to select the following:

   a. The symbol for the data points on that curve. Different symbols must be used for each curve if you are printing in black and white.

   b. The font size for the symbol. (The default value of 10 is too large; try using 6.)

   c. Connect data points with straight lines (usually, unless a trendline is to be shown).

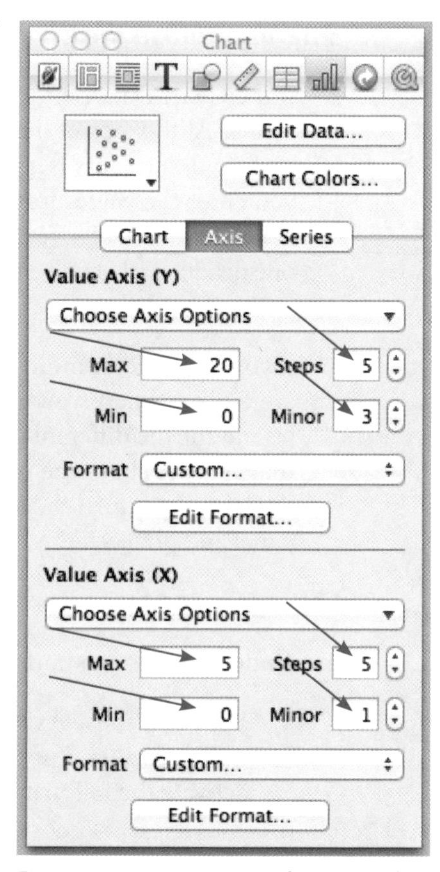

Figure 7-22. Pages '09 scale and gridlines options in the Inspector panel.

Final Cleanup

6. A default font size of 12 pt. is used in Pages for all the titles and axis values. This is too large. To change it, click on one of the title fields in the graph and set the font size to 10 pt. The font sizes are set separately for the five individual fields for the axis scales, axis labels, and legend.

7. If the legend seems spaced too far away from the graph, do the following. Click on your graph. Then, in the Inspector panel, select the Wrap (object placement) menu icon, as shown in Figure 7-23. At the bottom of that menu panel, you should see that the Object Causes Wrap box is checked, and there is a value entered in the Extra Space field. Adjusting this value will change the spacing between the legend and the graph. For the graph shown in Figure 7-24, I set the Extra Space value to 0.

8. As you write your report, you can click and drag the graph to place it where you want in the document. The legend is a separate object in the document and has to be moved separately.

The completed graph used for this example is shown in Figure 7-24. The label and title are typed in Pages just above the graph.

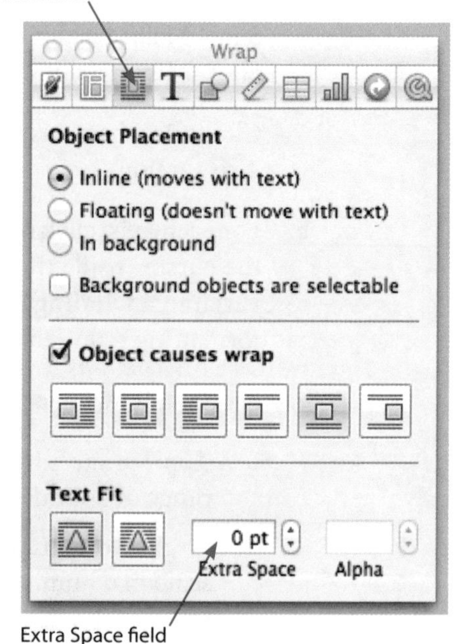

Figure 7-23. Pages '09 setting axis options in the Inspector panel.

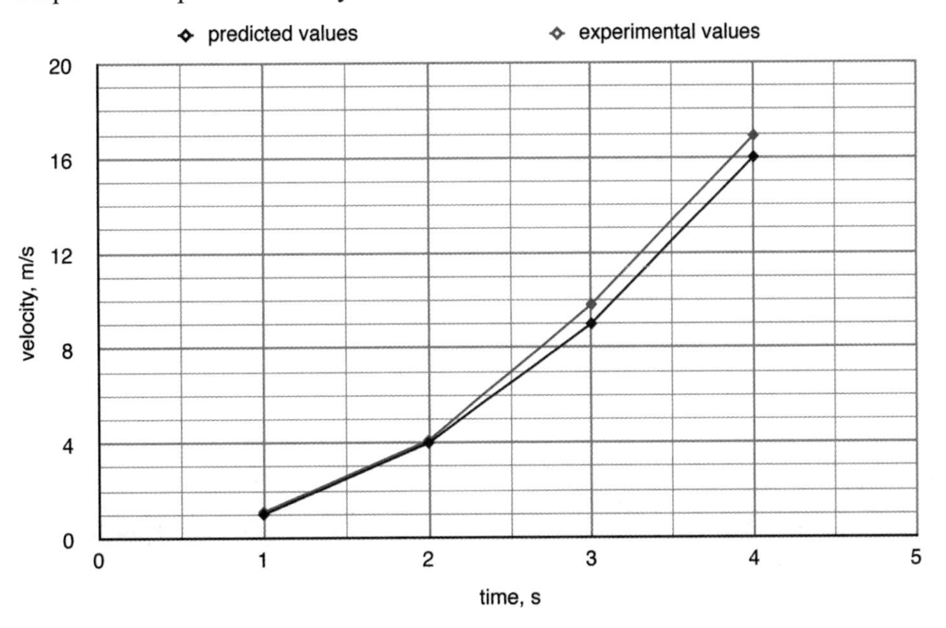

Figure 7-24. Pages '09 completed graph with label and title.

Adding a Trendline

9. To add a trendline to a data set, click on the *Series* tab in the Inspector and then activate the Advanced drop-down menu, as shown in Figure 7-25.

10. You must select the type of trendline. Linear is the choice when you wish to show the line resulting from a linear regression. You can check the Show Equation field to see the equation for the trendline that will be shown on the graph (to see the slope or y-intercept). The equation shows up on the graph itself. Once you record the equation in your lab journal or report, you may or may not want it to be displayed on the graph.

11. After the trendline is displayed, you need to adjust its appearance. Click on the line. Then in the Inspector panel, click on the Graphic Inspector icon at the top, as shown in Figure 7-26. In the Stroke area, reduce the point size from the default to 1 pt. Just below, deselect the Shadow box.

12. An example graph with a linear regression trendline is shown in Figure 7-27.

7.8 Creating Graphs with Microsoft Excel on a Mac (Office 2008)

Follow these instructions if you have the Mac version of Office 2008 installed on your Mac. You can create your graph in Excel and then copy-paste it into your Word or Pages report file.

Initial Setup

These first few steps are illustrated in Figure 7-28.

1. In Excel, list the values of the independent variable (horizontal axis) in order from least to greatest in column A and their corresponding values of the dependent variable (vertical axis) in column B.

   Note: If you are constructing two curves on the same graph (such as predicted and experimental curves), use column A for a single set of X-values. Then enter Y-values for the different data sets

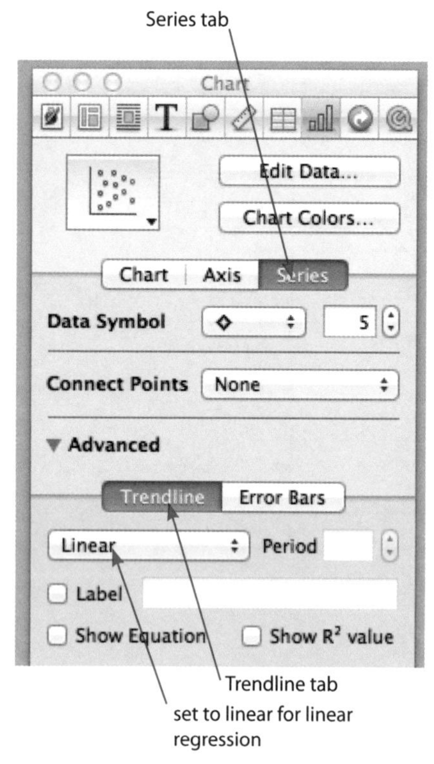

Figure 7-25. Pages '09 activating the trendline.

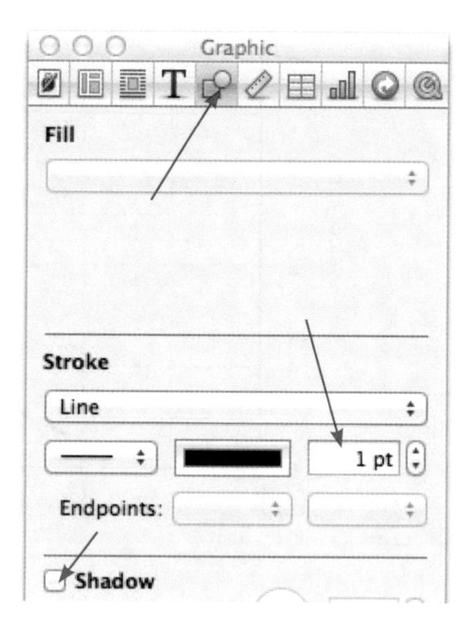

Figure 7-26. Pages '09 adjusting trendline appearance.

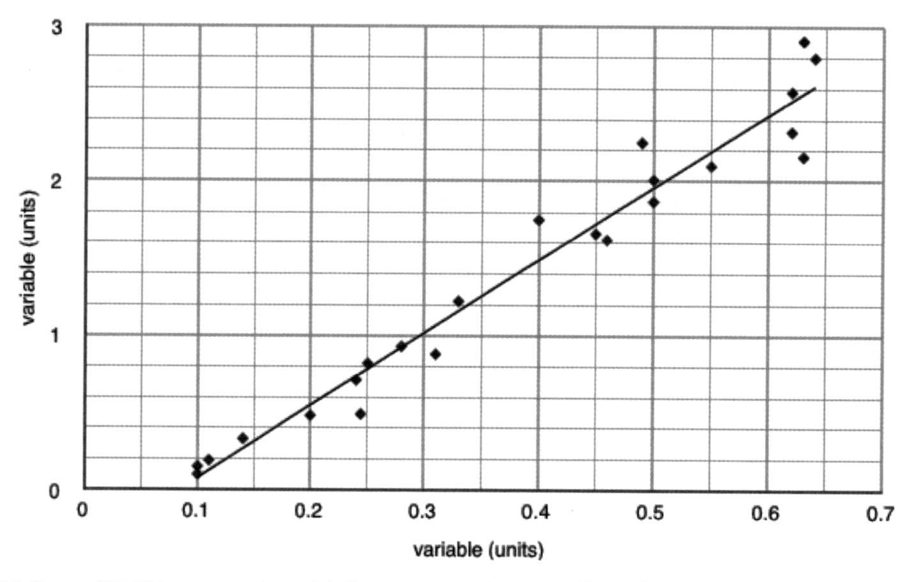

Figure 7-27. Pages '09 XY scatter plot with linear regression trendline shown.

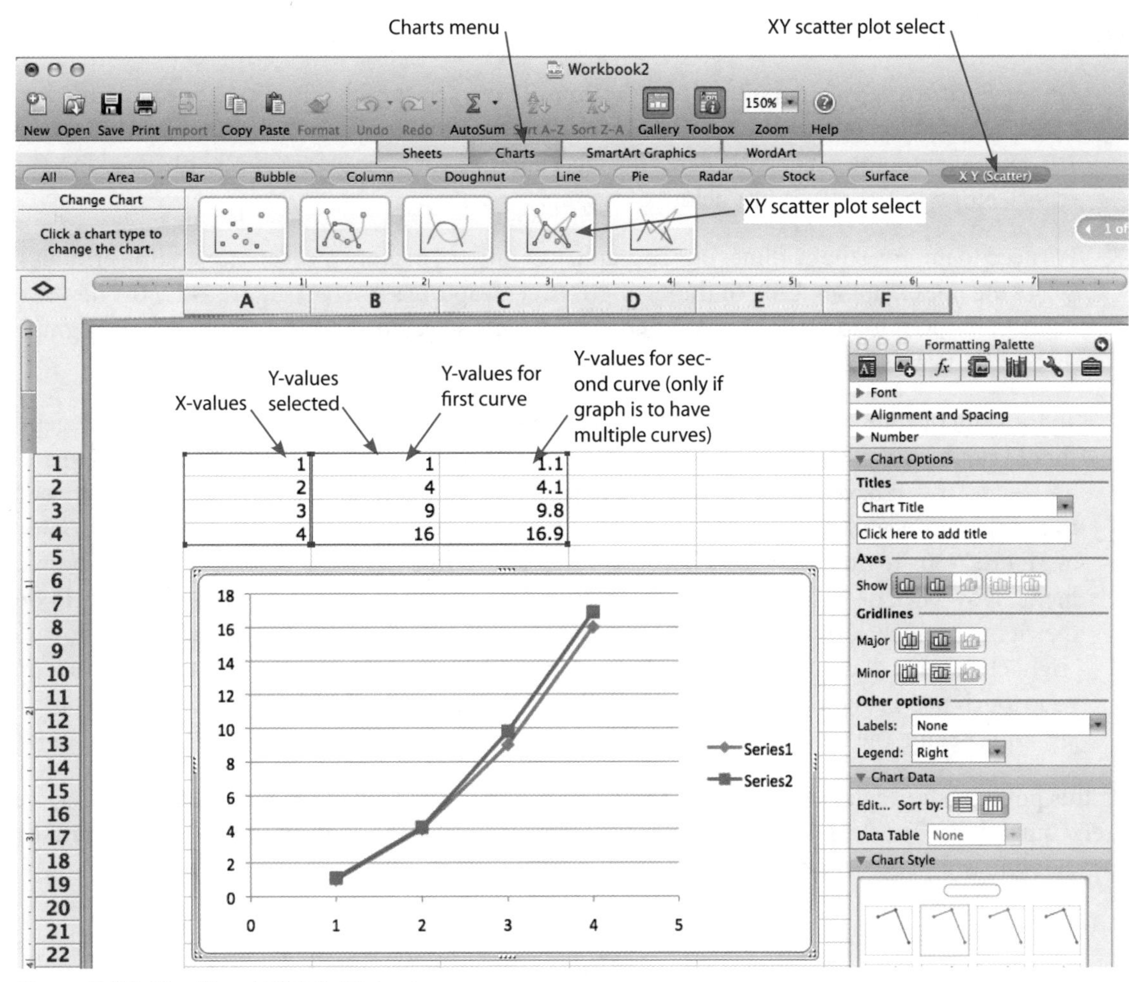

Figure 7-28. Mac/Excel 2008 initial setup.

in columns B, C, etc. For example, enter the predicted values for the independent variable in column B and your experimental values in column C.

2. Select and highlight all of these values by clicking and dragging the mouse.

3. Click on CHARTS in the toolbar.

4. From the list of chart types near the tool bar (All, Area, Bar, Bubble, etc.), click on XY (Scatter).

5. From the sample charts shown, select the appropriate type of graph and your graph will appear in a window on the screen. Three of the graph options show the data points and two do not. Always use a graph that displays the data points. Typically, you should choose the graph that connects the dots with straight lines (the fourth selection). Your instructor may wish for you to use the one without any lines.

   Note: For lower level courses, you should probably stay away from the graphs that generate curved lines between data points. This automatic curve-fitting feature can generate some weird, confusing curves. The curve-fitting graphs are more appropriate for certain applications in upper level classes.

   When the graph appears, the Formatting Palette should appears as well, as shown in Figure 7-28. If it does not, click on View in the upper menu bar, then select Formatting Palette.

Detailed Configuration

6. On the Formatting Palette under Chart Options/Titles, select each of the axes one at a time and enter the variable name and units of measure, using the standard formatting described in Section 7-2. Do not enter the Chart Title here. The label and title for your graph should be typed in your report, either just above or just below your graph.

7. We need to improve the gridlines on the graph. Just under Titles are the icons for adding gridlines. Select the ones that look best. In the example screen capture shown in Figure 7-29, the first two icons under Major and the first icon under Minor are selected. Select the icons for your graph that make it easiest to read.

8. To the right of your graph is a default legend. If you have only one curve on the graph, the legend should not be there. With only one curve, the legend reads "Series 1." Click on this legend and hit Delete. If you have two or more curves on the graph, the legend is necessary and you need to change the legend descriptions to describe what the curves actually represent, as illustrated in Figure 7-30. To do this, "right click" on the legend, and click on Select Data from the popup menu. Now click on Series 1 on the left and type in the name for Series 1 in the Name field on the right. Then click on Series 2 and type in the name for Series 2. (If you don't know how to "right click" on a Mac, get someone to show you. All Macs can do it, but you may need to set up your touch pad or mouse to make it work. By default, control-click [holding down the control key and clicking the mouse] is right click.)

At this point, your graph is all there and should look like the example in Figure 7-29. However, we aren't quite done. The defaults for the weights of the curves and the fonts in the titles are too flashy for scientific work and need to be toned down.

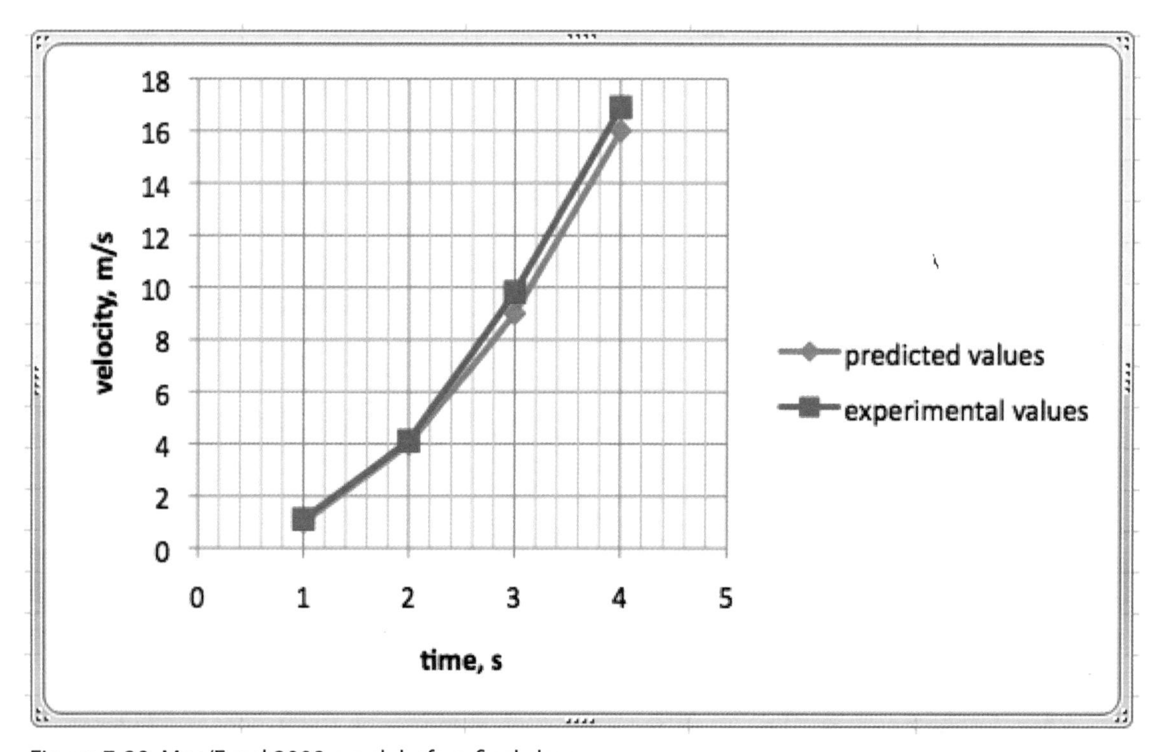

Figure 7-29. Mac/Excel 2008 graph before final cleanup.

Final Cleanup

9. Do this for each of the axis labels: Click on the label. Then on the Formatting Palette under the Font settings, turn off the bold by clicking on the B. The font sizes should be 10 pt.

10. To reduce the line weight of the curve(s) on the graph, first position your cursor right over one of the data points on the curve and double click. From the popup menu, select Weights and Arrows. Under Line Style, click on the tab for Style and change the weight from the default to 1.5 pt or 1 pt. Then click Okay. Do the same thing for the other curves, if any. After editing each curve click somewhere else on the graph to deselect the curve. Except for the graph title, your graph should now look like the graph shown in Figure 7-31.

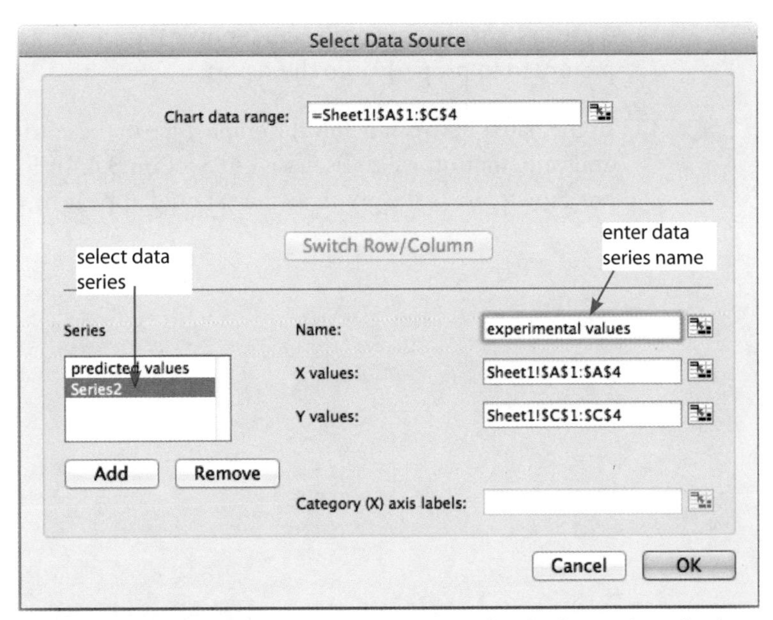

Figure 7-30. Mac/Excel 2008 setting names for the legend (multiple curve graphs only).

11. The graph is now ready to paste into the report. Place the cursor inside the graph in the white space and click. Then select Edit/Copy. Go to the word processor file containing your report and place the cursor where you want the graph to go. Then select Edit/Paste. Voila! You have a nice professional looking graph in your report. If you are pasting the graph into a Word document, the Arial fonts on the graph will all switch to Times when you paste the graph into Word. This is fine. If you are pasting the graph into a Pages file, the fonts will remain the same. You can click

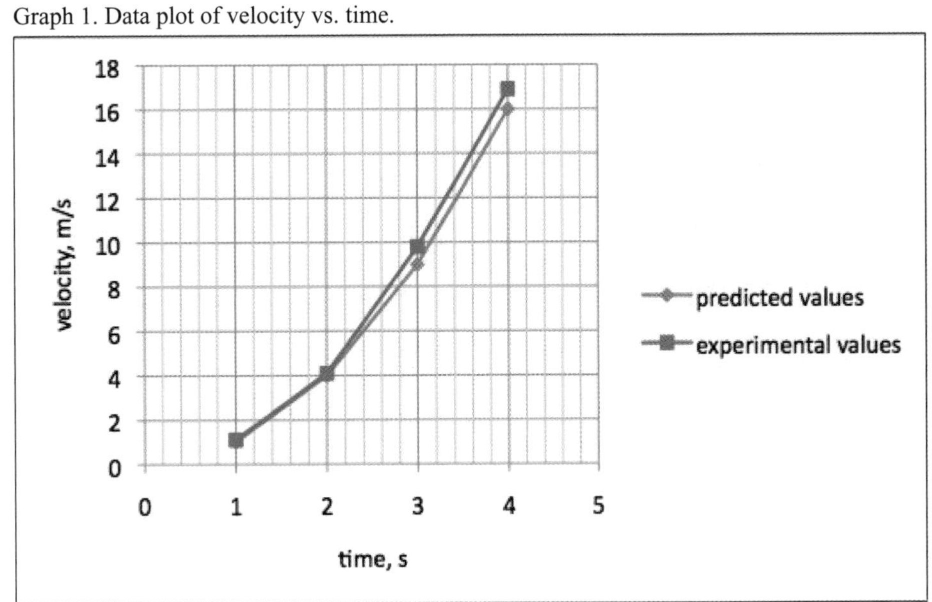

Figure 7-31. Mac/Excel 2008 final graph.

on the picture and place the cursor over the corner and click and drag to enlarge or shrink your picture to fit properly into the report.

12. Immediately above or below the graph, type in the label and title of your graph using the formatting and punctuation rules discussed in Section 3.4. In Figure 7-31, the label and title of the graph are shown above the graph as they should appear in your report.

Chapter 8
Common Lab Report Deficiencies

Here are some deficiencies I have seen over and over in student reports. You should work hard to avoid these.

8.1 Deficiencies in Report Text

1. Inadequate development or clarity of background

   The background section must describe the relationship between the physical laws that apply to the subject under study. The background must also describe the lab activity itself. In addition to describing the physical laws and equations, students should describe why the particular method or procedure used in the lab activity is appropriate for investigating the phenomenon at hand. It is important that the logic of the theoretical explanation should be clear, including why certain equations are introduced, how they relate to the theory, and what role they play in the experiment.

   As discussed in Section 4.4, there are four key components to include in the Background section. Make sure you address each of them.

2. Unclear descriptions of procedure

   The procedure should be described with enough clarity so that someone else could follow it to replicate the experiment. Replication of scientific results is an important part of science and new "discoveries" that are not repeatable will not be accepted by the scientific community. The key in this section is to make your description clear, unambiguous, and thorough.

3. Inadequate discussion of causes of percent difference

   Your comments in this section depend on two main factors. The first is how large your percent difference values are. This factor must be addressed by anyone writing a report. The second is whether you calculated uncertainty values (typically the sample standard deviation used to construct uncertainty bars on a graph). This factor only applies to more advanced students using experimental uncertainty to assess their results.

   If your percent difference calculation indicates a very small difference between your prediction and results, then you don't have much explaining to do. If you calculated uncertainty values and the percent difference is smaller than the uncertainty, then you can simply say "the results are within experimental uncertainty." If you did not calculate uncertainty values, then you will have to judge whether the percent difference requires an explanation. For typical equipment used in high school science labs, a percent difference below 5% may be regarded as a result not requiring much explanation. You can simply write that the percent difference *appears* to be within experimental uncertainty. However, if you are using a highly accurate apparatus with highly accurate and precise measurement tools, then the benchmark for explanation might more like 3%. But if you are using equipment this accurate, you should probably be calculating the experimental uncertainty and using that as a benchmark.

   If your percent difference values are higher than the benchmarks discussed in the previous paragraph, then you must seek to identify and explain why. As explained in Chapter 6, potential sources of error should be analyzed and compared to the calculated percent difference. If the percent difference was 7%, then minor sources of error should be sought. If the percent difference was 30%, then the student should ignore miniscule sources of error and focus instead on significant sources of error. The discussion should reflect this sort of analysis. If there is wide variation in certain measurements, these will probably contribute the most to large amounts of error.

4. Poor style

   Study the style guidelines in Chapter 3 and put time into learning how to write well in a technical paper. Watch out for slang or casual language, inappropriate use of personal pronouns, inappropriate verb forms, and poorly named figures.

5. Unsubstantiated claims

   Discussions of error and other experimental results should be based on experimental data and scientific reasoning. You must not make claims without supporting evidence. An example of an unsubstantiated claim is declaring a cause of error without any explanation, such as writing "Although we couldn't measure the friction, friction was the cause of error in our setup." Another example is claiming that a law was confirmed even though the percent difference was high, as in "Even though we had a percent difference of 45%, the law of conservation of energy was still confirmed."

6. Inclusion of trivial detail

   Leave out trivial details in descriptions and calculations. Examples of such trivia include descriptions of how to assemble simple lab equipment, definitions of common terms, and instructions on how to use standard equipment items.

8.2 Missing Content

7. Missing sections

   Your report must include each of the sections described in Chapter 4. The only exception is that students are usually not required to include an abstract until they reach upper-level high school courses. Juniors or seniors in high school and college students should include an abstract.

8. Missing references to tables, graphs, and figures

   Always refer the reader to every table, graph, and figure by actually writing something in the text such as, "The experimental data are shown in Tables 2a and 2b," "The calculated results are plotted in Graph 2," "The experimental setup is shown in Figure 1," or another statement of this type.

9. Missing Data

   If you took data, it must be presented in the report in the original units of measure. If you calculated any values such as predicted values, experimental error, or uncertainty these must all be presented as well. Always place the data in a table.

8.3 Incorrect Formatting or Appearance

10. Incorrect punctuation in labels and titles of tables, graphs, or figures.

    Punctuation of labels and titles should conform to the rules discussed in Section 3.4. Formatting for axis labels in graphs should conform to the standards discussed in Section 7.2.

11. Inadequate figures

    Tiny little figures that do not really show how the apparatus was put together are not helpful and should not appear in a technical paper. The paper should either include an explanation detailed enough to allow the setup of the apparatus to be understood without a diagram, or a diagram or photo large and detailed enough to actually show how the apparatus was used in the experiment. If diagrams are drawn by hand, they should be very carefully and neatly prepared, scanned, and digitally pasted into your report. Now that digital cameras are nearly ubiquitous (or mobile phones with cameras), hand drawn diagrams are less called for. If you need a diagram of the setup, consider how well you can draw one, and if you can't draw it well, consider using a photograph. However, if the setup has particular features that are complex and not represented by the photograph, a careful sketch of these features might still be necessary. If you draw a sketch by hand, you should scan it and insert it into your report digitally, with an appropriate label and title. Do not draw a sketch directly onto the report print out.

12. Printing and assembly errors

    Your report should be properly printed and include the correct pages in the proper order. If your printer's toner was running out and the pages look faded, you should either fix your printer or print the report elsewhere.

    You should check through the pages of your report to make sure that there are no missing pages and no pages included that don't belong there.

13. Incorrect page breaks

    You should not allow a page break to separate a section heading in your report from the first line of the next paragraph. There are a couple of ways to address this. The sophisticated way is by the use of paragraph styles with appropriate settings. The quick and unsophisticated way is to insert a page break right before the heading to force it to the next page.

    You should also not allow the title of a table, graph, or figure to be separated from the element it refers to by a page break.

    You also should not allow a table to break across pages. If you need to, place a page break in front of the table's title so that the title and table both go to the next page.

Chapter 9
Example Lab Reports

The following example reports illustrate how the guidelines for style, formatting, and content of lab reports are applied.

Example 1-A: Boiling Points of Water-Glycol Solutions

This example of a simple experiment illustrates the expectations for a report written by someone relatively new to lab report writing. Included are data tables, a basic graph, one reference, and basic text for each of the main sections in the report.

Example 1-B: Boiling Points of Water-Glycol Solutions

This report is an enhanced version of the report in Example 1-A and represents expectations for students who have already written a few reports. Using the same data and the same experimental procedures, this report is based on a more sophisticated purpose, and includes more advanced graphing (uncertainty bars showing $\pm 1s$ on the data points) and a more sophisticated analysis. The report also includes an Abstract. The Results section includes observations about the individual measurements and what these may imply about the measurement instruments used in the experiment. Most students will be able to write reports at this level during their second or third year, although accelerated students should be able to produce this type of analysis by the end of their first year.

Example 2: Investigating Charles' Law

This example is much more sophisticated, and represents work that students should be able to perform at the junior or senor level. The report includes an Abstract. The Background and Discussion sections are quite detailed and show great care in analysis. The Background section includes a short historical paragraph outlining when and by whom the physical laws pertaining to the experiment were discovered. The Discussion of results involves a detailed analysis of the percent difference, and solid speculation as to its cause. Formatting shows appropriate ways of dealing with theoretical equations, including equation numbering, which can simplify discussion in a complex analysis. Graphical presentation of data includes the theoretical curve on the graph with the experimental results.

Example 3: Genetics of Organisms

This report was modified from the AP Biology Lab 7: Genetics of *Drosophila* protocol provided in the Carolina Scientific kit. This example represents typical discovery-driven experiments common in the study of biology. This report includes an Abstract (a rather long one), a detailed technical description of the procedure, and a very advanced analysis that includes complex charts showing experimental results.

Physical Science Laboratory

Boiling Point of Water-Glycol Solutions

Author:	Ann T. Friese
Team Members:	Bernie Bunsen, Sy Linder
Date of Experiment:	September 12, 2014
Date Report Submitted:	September 17, 2014
Class:	Physical Science, 2nd Period
	Mr. Ford, Instructor

Purpose

The purpose of this experiment was to investigate how the boiling point of water changed with increasing concentrations of ethylene glycol added in solution. An off-the-shelf antifreeze packaged as a 50/50 water-ethylene glycol solution was used.

Background

Automobile engines typically use a coolant consisting of a mixture of 50% water and 50% antifreeze. Commercially available antifreeze products consist primarily of ethylene glycol, with other agents added to prevent rust in the engine. Some antifreezes are sold full strength and need to be mixed with water in the engine. Others are sold in a 50/50 mixture and may be added directly to the cooling system without adding any water.

Since the freezing point of ethylene glycol is lower than the freezing point of water, the antifreeze helps prevent the engine coolant from freezing in the winter. Additionally, the boiling point of ethylene glycol is higher than the boiling point of water. This means the engine coolant can also get hotter in the summer without boiling, compared to plain water.

The boiling points of water and ethylene glycol are 100°C and 198°C, respectively (1). Our team prepared solutions of ethylene glycol and water of varying concentrations from 0% to 50% and measured their boiling points. We assumed that as the concentration of ethylene glycol increased the boiling point of the solution would increase linearly from 100°C to 198°C. Our hypothesis was that the boiling points of the solutions would increase linearly with concentration, and at a 50% concentration the boiling point of the solution would be half way between the boiling points of water and ethylene glycol, or 149°C.

Experimental Procedure

Equipment and materials used in the experiment were as follows:

support rod (4)
rod clamp (4)
burner ring (4)
burner pad (4)

Bunsen burner (4)
gas hose (4)
tongs
butane lighter
graduated cylinder, 100 mL (4)
graduated cylinder, 250 mL
beaker, 2000 mL
beaker, 1000 mL
beaker, 500 mL
beaker, 400 mL (4)
stirring rod
digital multimeter, Fluke 179, with 80-BK temperature probe
data collector, Pasco Explorer GLX with temperature sensor (2)
antifreeze, Super S brand, 50/50 prediluted (1 gal)
tap water

The team set up four experiment stations, each with a Bunsen burner, burner ring, burner pad, and other items necessary to boil water in a 400 mL beaker. We only had three devices for measuring temperature, so we used a Fluke 179 at Station 1, a Pasco meter at Station 2, and another Pasco meter to measure temperatures at both Stations 3 and 4. Each time we inserted the temperature sensor into a new liquid we were careful to adjust the probe so that its tip was approximately in the center of the liquid in the beaker and not touching the side or bottom of the beaker.

We decided to use 200.0 mL of liquid for all solutions. After an initial data collection run with 200.0 mL of tap water at each station, we then prepared solutions with ethylene glycol. The first solution was a 10% concentration ethylene glycol solution, containing 20.0 mL of ethylene glycol. Since the antifreeze was a 50/50 mixture, 40.0 mL of antifreeze contained 20.0 mL of ethylene glycol and 20.0 mL of water. Using the graduated cylinders and carefully measuring liquid quantities to the nearest 1/10 mL, we added 40.0 mL antifreeze and 160.0 mL water to each of four 400 mL beakers to prepare the 10% solutions. During the measuring of the liquids, all members of the team were careful to read the volume at the bottom of the meniscus and to avoid parallax error. We then heated the four solutions until each was at a rolling boil, at which time we recorded the temperature reading.

We repeated this process for each of the other sets of solutions. Quantities of liquid used for all trials are shown in Table 1.

Table 1. Liquid quantities for solutions of different concentration.

Concentration (%)	Water Volume (mL)	50/50 Antifreeze Volume (mL)	Total Volume (mL)
0	200.0	0.0	200.0
10	160.0	40.0	200.0
20	120.0	80.0	200.0
30	80.0	120.0	200.0
40	40.0	160.0	200.0
50	0.0	200.0	200.0

Results

Temperature data for all of the solutions, as well as the mean boiling temperature for each concentration, are shown in Table 2.

Table 2. Boiling points of ethylene glycol solutions.

Concentration (%)	Station 1 Fluke 179 Temp. (°C)	Station 2 Pasco #1 Temp. (°C)	Station 3 Pasco #2 Temp. (°C)	Station 4 Pasco #2 Temp. (°C)	Mean Temp. (°C)
0%	101.0	101.5	101.8	99.7	101.0
10%	102.8	102.8	100.0	102.7	102.1
20%	104.3	104.4	105.1	104.3	104.5
30%	105.1	109.0	107.9	107.3	107.3
40%	106.6	109.4	108.6	109.8	108.6
50%	110.0	112.9	113.5	116.4	113.2

Discussion

Graph 1 depicts the mean boiling temperature for each solution concentration. As indicated by the graph, the mean boiling point does appear to increase linearly with temperature, because the data points lie very nearly in a straight line. This trend appears to confirm the first part of our team's hypothesis, that the boiling points of the solutions would increase linearly with temperature.

Graph 1. Boiling temperatures of ethylene glycol solutions.

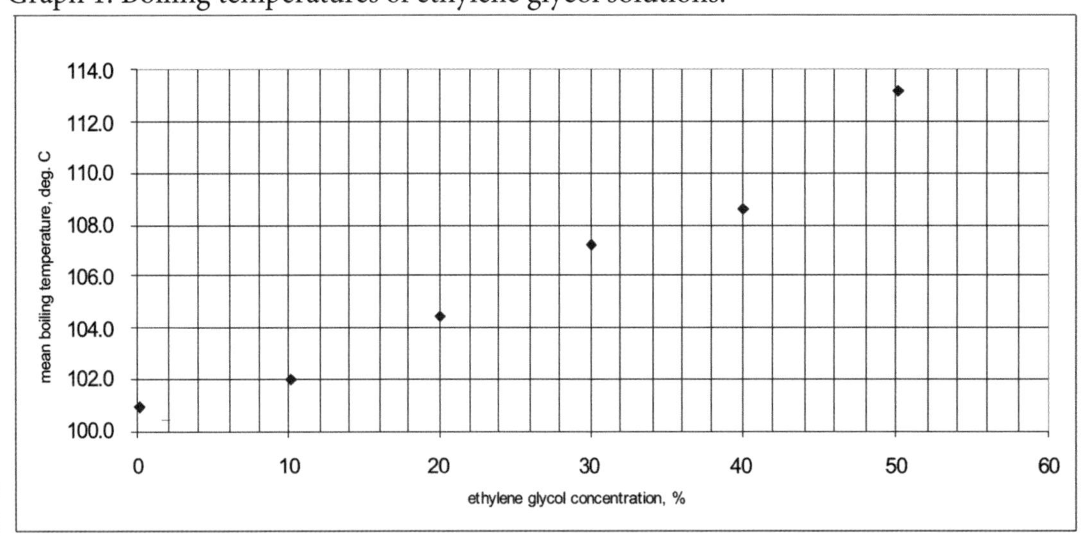

However, the second part of our team's hypothesis was that at 50% concentration, which is half way between 0% and 100%, the solution boiling point would be half way between the boiling points of water and ethylene glycol, or 149°C. With a mean boiling point of 113.2°C at 50% concentration, this clearly was not the case. We calculated the percent difference using the standard equation

$$\text{percent difference} = \frac{|\text{predicted/accepted value} - \text{experimental value}|}{\text{predicted value}} \times 100\%$$

Our team calculated a percent difference of

$$\frac{|149 - 113.2|}{149} \times 100\% = 24\%$$

This difference between our prediction and our results is much larger than expected.

Discussions of this discrepancy led us to identify three factors that may have influenced our results. First, we noted that the label on the antifreeze container indicates that the antifreeze was not, in fact, a pure solution of ethylene glycol and water. The label mentions "rust inhibitors," but does not provide any details about what these components might be or how concentrated they are. Without knowing exactly what was in the solution, we cannot be sure that the rust inhibitors didn't influence the boiling points. In fact, they probably did, but we cannot say by how much.

Second, it is possible that the prediluted antifreeze solution did not contain 50% ethylene glycol as the label claimed.

Third, it is possible that the trend in the boiling points from pure water to pure ethylene glycol is not linear after all as we hypothesized. It seems reasonable that the trend would be linear, but without any data above 50% concentration we cannot be sure. In fact, close inspection of Graph 1 indicates that there may be a very slight upward curve in the data, implying that the boiling point may increase faster as the concentration nears 100%. Again, without data above 50% we cannot be sure.

Conclusion

Our results are inconclusive. Our data do appear to indicate a linear trend in boiling point as concentration increases. However, the high percent difference for our highest solution concentration indicates that unknown factors are influencing the solution boiling points. Future experiments should include data for solution concentrations all the way up to 100% ethylene glycol. This would require use of an ethylene glycol product that was not diluted 50/50, and should settle the question of whether the temperature trend is linear or not. Additionally, this experiment should be performed using pure ethylene glycol rather than commercial antifreeze products. All antifreeze products include rust inhibitors that probably influence the boiling point.

References

1. *CRC Handbook of Physics and Chemistry*, 68th ed. (Boca Raton: CRC Press, 1987).

Chemistry Laboratory

Boiling Point of Water-Glycol Solutions

Author:	Ann T. Friese
Team Members:	Bernie Bunsen, Sy Linder
Date of Experiment:	September 12, 2014
Date Report Submitted:	September 17, 2014
Class:	Chemistry, 2nd Period Mr. Ford, Instructor

Abstract

Ethylene glycol solutions at varying concentrations were tested to determine boiling point. Boiling points increased linearly ($r = 0.983$) up to the maximum tested concentration of 50%, which was consistent with the experimental hypothesis. However, the boiling point predicted by the regression for pure ethylene glycol differed from the accepted value by 37%. Additional experiments are recommended to determine the source of this large difference.

Purpose

The purpose of this experiment was to investigate how the boiling point of water changed with increasing concentrations of ethylene glycol added in solution. Additionally, our team sought to use an off-the-shelf antifreeze packaged as a 50/50 water-ethylene glycol solution to estimate the boiling point of pure ethylene glycol.

Background

Automobile engines typically use a coolant consisting of a mixture of 50% water and 50% antifreeze. Commercially available antifreeze products consist primarily of ethylene glycol, with other agents added to prevent rust in the engine. Some antifreezes are sold full strength and need to be mixed with water in the engine. Others are sold in a 50/50 mixture and may be added directly to the cooling system without adding any water.

Since the freezing point of ethylene glycol is lower than the freezing point of water, the antifreeze helps prevent the engine coolant from freezing in the winter. Additionally, the boiling point of ethylene glycol is higher than the boiling point of water. This means the engine coolant can also get hotter in the summer without boiling, compared to plain water.

The boiling points of water and ethylene glycol are 100°C and 198°C, respectively (1). Our team prepared solutions of ethylene glycol and water of varying concentrations from 0% to 50% and measured their boiling points. We assumed that as the concentration of ethylene glycol increased the boiling point of the solution would increase linearly from 100°C to 198°C. Our hypothesis was that the boiling points of the solutions would increase linearly with concentration. Further, we hypothesized that the line of best fit through our temperature data for solutions up to 50% concentration would indicate that the boiling point of pure ethylene glycol would be 198°C.

Experimental Procedure

Equipment and materials used in the experiment were as follows:

support rod (4)
rod clamp (4)
burner ring (4)
burner pad (4)
Bunsen burner (4)
gas hose (4)
tongs
butane lighter
graduated cylinder, 100 mL (4)
graduated cylinder, 250 mL
beaker, 2000 mL
beaker, 1000 mL
beaker, 500 mL
beaker, 400 mL (4)
stirring rod
digital multimeter, Fluke 179, with 80-BK temperature probe
data collector, Pasco Explorer GLX with temperature sensor (2)
antifreeze, Super S brand, 50/50 prediluted (1 gal)
tap water

The team set up four experiment stations, each with a Bunsen burner, burner ring, burner pad, and other items necessary to boil water in a 400 mL beaker. We only had three devices for measuring temperature, so we used a Fluke 179 at Station 1, a Pasco meter at Station 2, and another Pasco meter to measure temperatures at both Stations 3 and 4. Each time we inserted the temperature sensor into a new liquid, we were careful to adjust the probe so that its tip was approximately in the center of the liquid in the beaker and not touching the side or bottom of the beaker.

We decided to use 200.0 mL of liquid for all solutions. After an initial data collection run with 200.0 mL of tap water at each station, we prepared solutions with ethylene glycol. The first solution was a 10% concentration ethylene glycol solution, containing 20.0 mL of ethylene glycol. Since the antifreeze was a 50/50 mixture, 40.0 mL of antifreeze contained 20.0 mL of ethylene glycol and 20.0 mL of water. Using the graduated cylinders and carefully measuring liquid quantities to the nearest 1/10 mL, we added 40.0 mL antifreeze and 160.0 mL water to each of four 400 mL beakers to prepare the 10% solutions. During the measuring of the liquids, all members of the team were careful to read the volume at the bottom of the meniscus and to avoid parallax error. We then heated the four solutions until each was at a rolling boil, at which time we recorded the temperature reading.

We repeated this process for each of the other sets of solutions. Quantities of liquid used for all trials are shown in Table 1.

Table 1. Liquid quantities for solutions of different concentration.

Concentration (%)	Water Volume (mL)	50/50 Antifreeze Volume (mL)	Total Volume (mL)
0	200.0	0.0	200.0
10	160.0	40.0	200.0
20	120.0	80.0	200.0
30	80.0	120.0	200.0
40	40.0	160.0	200.0
50	0.0	200.0	200.0

Results

Temperature data for all of the solutions, as well as the mean temperature and standard deviations for each concentration, are shown in Table 2. We noted that there seemed to be noticeable inaccuracy with the temperature measurement instruments. For example, every time the Pasco #2 probe was removed from the boiling liquid at Station 3 and inserted into the supposedly identical boiling liquid at Station 4, the measurement would fluctuate wildly for several seconds, above and below the expected reading, and then settle on a value that was one to three degrees different from the reading at station 3. Although these differences were unexpected, they appeared to be within the temperature measurement tolerance specified by the manufacturer.

Table 2. Boiling points of ethylene glycol solutions.

Concentration (%)	Station 1 Fluke 179 Temp. (°C)	Station 2 Pasco #1 Temp. (°C)	Station 3 Pasco #2 Temp. (°C)	Station 4 Pasco #2 Temp. (°C)	Mean Temp. (°C)	s (°C)
0%	101.0	101.5	101.8	99.7	101.0	0.93
10%	102.8	102.8	100.0	102.7	102.1	1.38
20%	104.3	104.4	105.1	104.3	104.5	0.39
30%	105.1	109.0	107.9	107.3	107.3	1.64
40%	106.6	109.4	108.6	109.8	108.6	1.42
50%	110.0	112.9	113.5	116.4	113.2	2.62

Discussion

Graph 1 depicts the mean boiling temperature for each solution concentration. Measurement uncertainties are indicated by the $\pm 1s$ bars shown at each data point. As indicated by the graph, the mean boiling point does appear to increase linearly with temperature, because the data points lie very nearly in a straight line. A linear regression on these values gives a very strong linear correlation coefficient of $r = 0.983$. This trend appears to confirm the first part of our team's hypothesis, namely that the boiling points of the solutions would increase linearly with temperature.

Graph 1. Boiling points of ethylene glycol solutions with uncertainty bars at $\pm 1s$.

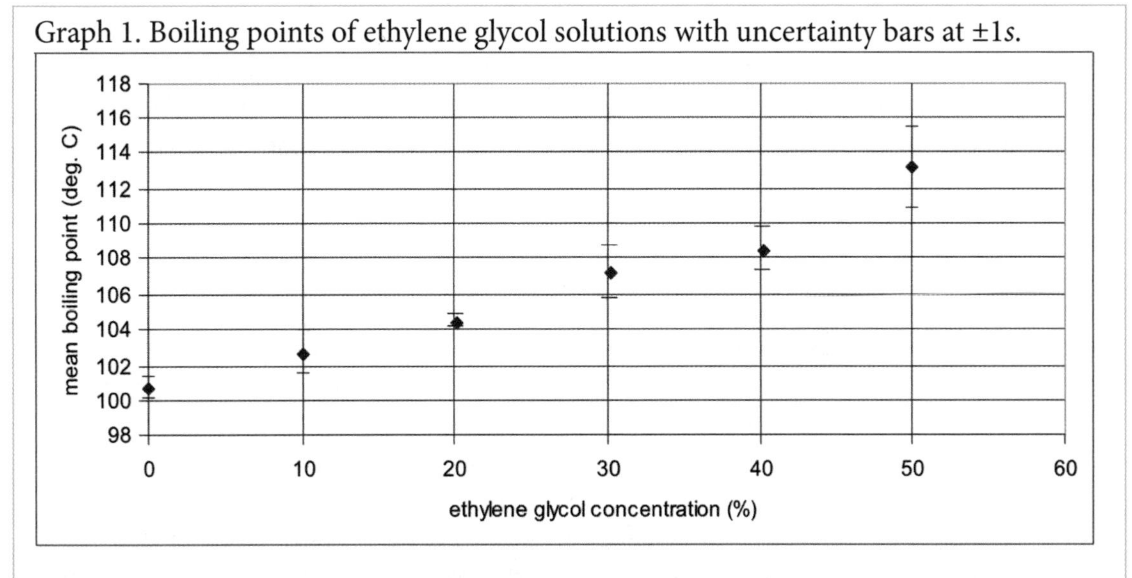

However, the second part of our team's hypothesis was that a linear regression of the data up through 50% concentration would indicate a boiling point of 198°C for pure ethylene glycol. The linear regression for the mean boiling point values is $\hat{y} = 0.238x + 100.2$, where $\hat{y}$ is the predicted boiling point and x is the percentage concentration. This equation yields a prediction at 100% concentration of 124.0°C. Extrapolations way beyond the data like this are generally frowned upon. In this case, we were using the assumption of linearity to predict the boiling point at a much higher temperature.

We calculated the percent difference for this prediction using the standard equation

$$\text{percent difference} = \frac{|\text{predicted/accepted value} - \text{experimental value}|}{\text{predicted value}} \times 100\%$$

Our team calculated a percent difference of

$$\frac{|198 - 124|}{198} \times 100\% = 37\%$$

This difference between our prediction and our results is much larger than expected.

Discussions of this discrepancy led us to identify three factors that may have influenced our results. First, we noted that the label on the antifreeze container indicates that the antifreeze was not, in fact, a pure solution of ethylene glycol and water. The label mentions "rust inhibitors," but does not provide any details about what these components might be or how concentrated they are. Without knowing exactly what was in the solution, we cannot be sure that the rust inhibitors did not influence the boiling points. In fact, they probably did, but we cannot say by how much.

Second, it is possible that the prediluted antifreeze solution did not contain 50% ethylene glycol as the label claimed.

Third, it is possible that the trend in the boiling points from pure water to pure ethylene glycol is not linear after all as we hypothesized. It seems reasonable that the trend would be linear, but without any data above 50% concentration we cannot be sure. Although the linear correlation in the data of 0.983 is very strong, the trend could change dramatically for concentrations above 50%. Again, without data in that range we cannot say.

Conclusion

Our results are inconclusive. Our data do appear to indicate a linear trend in boiling point as concentration increases. However, the high percent difference for our highest solution concentration indicates that unknown factors are influencing the solution boiling points. Future experiments should include data for solution concentrations all the way up to 100% ethylene glycol. This would require use of an ethylene glycol product that was not diluted 50/50, and should settle the question of whether the temperature trend is linear or not. Additionally, this experiment should be performed using pure ethylene glycol rather than commercial antifreeze products. All antifreeze products include rust inhibitors that probably influence the boiling point.

References

1. *CRC Handbook of Physics and Chemistry*, 68th ed. (Boca Raton: CRC Press, 1987).

Physics Laboratory

Investigating Charles' Law

Author:	Imogen G. Lex
Team Members:	Phoebe Calor, August Flask
Date of Experiment:	February 15, 2014
Date Report Submitted:	February 22, 2014
Class:	Physics, 3rd Period Mr. J. P. Joule, Instructor

Abstract

A novel experimental method was used to allow a sample of air to expand freely with increasing temperature while holding pressure constant. As the air temperature was increased from –16°C to 76.9°C, measured volumes were within 2.31% of ideal gas law predictions up to approximately 40°C. Above 40°C, experimental data indicate that air departs from ideal gas behavior.

Purpose

The purpose of this experiment was to use Charles' Law for gases to make predictions regarding air volume vs. temperature and to compare the predictions to experimental data.

Background

Robert Boyle achieved one of the early milestones in the scientific exploration of the behavior of gases. In 1660, Boyle formulated his famous gas law, which stated that the pressure in a contained volume of gas varies in inverse proportion to the volume. Over a century later, French scientist Jacques Charles formulated the gas law that bears his name. Charles' Law states that the volume of a gas at constant pressure varies in direct proportion to the absolute temperature. Boyle's Law and Charles' Law were later combined to produce what is now known as the ideal gas law. (1)

In an ideal gas, volume, temperature and pressure are related according to the ideal gas law,

$$PV = nRT \qquad (1)$$

where:

P is the absolute gas pressure in pascals (Pa),

V is the gas volume in cubic meters (m^3),

n is the number of moles of the gas,

R is the ideal gas constant, equal to $8.314 \dfrac{\text{J}}{\text{mol} \cdot \text{K}}$, and

T is the gas temperature in kelvins (K).

Although no real gas obeys the ideal gas law perfectly, the relationship between the pressure, volume, and temperature of many gases will be described well by the ideal gas law if the gas is not near any phase changes and is not under extremes of pressure or temperature.

The ideal gas law may also be written as $\dfrac{V}{T} = \dfrac{nR}{P}$. If a fixed quantity of gas is held at a constant pressure, then n, R, and P are constants and the ideal gas law becomes $\dfrac{V}{T} = \text{constant}$, or $\dfrac{V_1}{T_1} = \dfrac{V_2}{T_2}$, which is Charles' Law. To investigate Charles' Law, a volume of a gas at a certain starting temperature may be compared with the gas volume at other temperatures. Charles' Law may be rewritten to express the volume of the gas as a function of temperature and the starting conditions:

$$V_2 = \frac{V_1}{T_1} \cdot T_2 \qquad (2)$$

From this form of the Charles' Law equation, it is clear that volume varies in direct proportion with temperature, with constant of proportionality equal to the ratio of initial volume (V_1) to initial temperature (T_1).

To measure gas volume, we used a test tube with precision volume markings. We inverted the test tube in a beaker of ethylene glycol so that there was a small air pocket in the top of the test tube. In this way, the pressure on the trapped air pocket was virtually constant as the air changed temperature, and the volume of the gas could change freely with temperature. The markings on the inverted test tube allowed us easily to read the volume of the gas. Ethylene glycol was used in the beaker rather than water so that we could begin taking data with gas temperatures below 0°C. Our hypothesis was that volume and temperature would vary in direct proportion to one another, as predicted by Charles' Law.

Experimental Procedure

Equipment and materials used in the experiment were as follows:

Fisher burner
beaker, 1500 mL
gas supply hose
burner ring
burner pad
support rod
digital multimeter, Fluke 179, with 80-BK temperature probe

test tube, 10 mL, graduated in 0.2 mL increments
test tube clamp
ethylene glycol, 50% solution, (antifreeze), approx. 1200 mL
freezer, standard kitchen-type consumer appliance

The day before the experiment, the beaker of 1200 mL ethylene glycol was placed in the freezer. On the day of the experiment, the beaker was removed from the freezer and placed on the burner pad on the burner ring above the burner supported by the support rod. The 10 mL test tube was inverted and supported with the test tube clamp. The test tube was adjusted so that it was completely immersed in and mostly filled with ethylene glycol, with a small but measurable air pocket in the top of the test tube. The test tube was adjusted so that it was close enough to the side of the beaker so that test tube volume readings could be taken from the outside by looking through the beaker. The air pocket in the top of the test tube constituted the initial volume of the gas. The temperature probe was inserted into the test tube so that its tip was up in the air pocket in the inverted test tube.

Placing the test tube under the liquid provided a nearly constant pressure seal on the gas trapped in the top of the test tube. The large volume beaker was used so that as the trapped air expanded, the rise of the liquid level in the beaker would be negligible. If there had been a significant rise in the liquid level, the pressure on the trapped gas would not have been constant. Initial volume and temperature readings were taken after the apparatus was completely set up, then the burner was ignited and the solution slowly warmed. Additional temperature and volume readings were recorded regularly until the volume was close to the maximum mark on the test tube.

Results

Initial conditions for the experimental setup are shown in Table 1. Data collected during the experiment are shown in Table 2, and are represented graphically in Graph 1.

Table 1. Air initial conditions.

Volume, V_1	5.2 mL
Temperature, T_1	−16.0°C

Table 2. Experimental air temperature and volume data.

temperature, °C	temperature, K	volume, mL
−16.0	257.2	5.2
−6.9	266.3	5.4
0.1	273.3	5.6
15.2	288.4	5.8
20.3	293.5	6.0
26.8	300.0	6.2
44.0	317.2	6.7
50.0	323.2	7.1
57.2	330.4	7.5
60.1	333.3	7.7
67.8	341.0	8.5
71.0	344.2	9.0
75.0	348.2	9.6
75.8	349.0	9.8
76.9	350.1	10.0

Discussion

Using the initial conditions and equation (2), we constructed a plot of the theoretical linear variation of volume with temperature for the gas. The equation for this theoretical variation, which must use temperature in absolute units, is

$$V_2 = \frac{V_1}{T_1} \cdot T_2 = \frac{5.2 \text{ mL}}{257.2 \text{ K}} \cdot T_2 = 0.0202 \ \frac{\text{mL}}{\text{K}} \cdot T_2 \qquad (3)$$

Graph 1. Air volume vs. temperature at constant pressure.

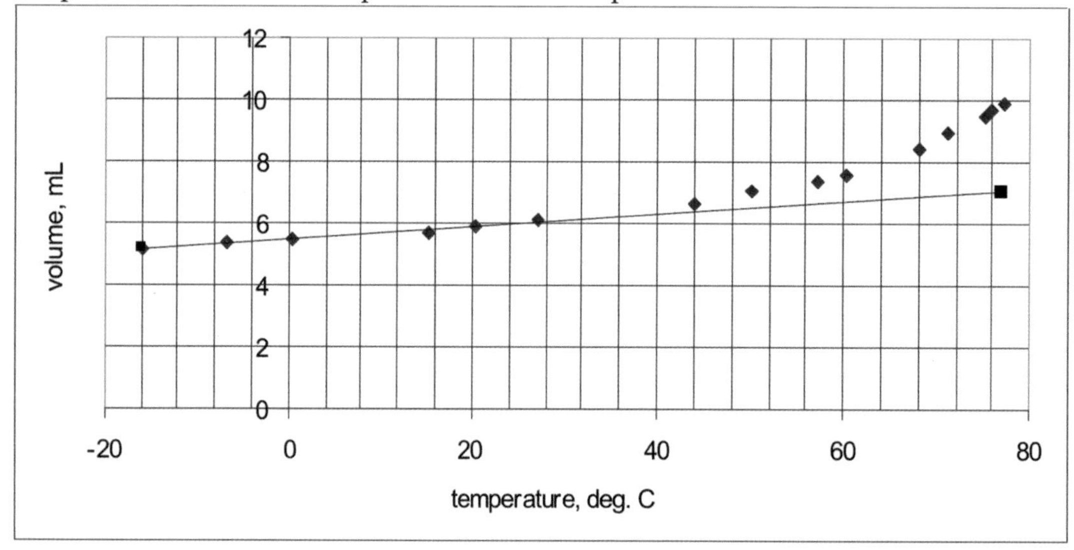

Using the highest temperature in the experiment, 76.9°C or 350.1 K, the theoretical volume corresponding to this temperature is 7.07 mL. The line in Graph 1 was plotted using the initial conditions and this theoretical volume corresponding to the final temperature of 350.1 K. As evident from Graph 1, experimental data corresponded very closely to theoretical variation for the lower half of the temperature range. Using equation (3), we calculated theoretical volumes for the temperature data. Then we calculated the percent differences for the volume values. The equation for calculating percent difference is

$$\text{percent difference} = \frac{|\text{predicted/accepted value} - \text{experimental value}|}{\text{predicted value}} \times 100\%$$

Table 3 shows the results of these calculations. Percent differences are very low, below 3%, up to around 30°C. Around 40°C, the experimental values begin noticeably diverging from the predicted values, and the percent difference begins increasing steadily after that up to a maximum of 41.4% at the highest temperature of 76.9°C.

In considering why the percent differences are so high in the upper temperature range, our team first speculated that the liquid level in the beaker might be rising slightly as the air expanded, causing variations in the air pressure on the trapped gas (air) sample. However, all else being equal, volume varies inversely with pressure, so that an increase in pressure due to deeper liquid in the beaker would have decreased the volume below the predicted values, whereas in this experiment the volume data were above the predicted values. Thus, changes in the depth of the liquid in the beaker were apparently not the cause of the percent differences.

Our team speculates that at temperatures above 40°C, the reduced density of the air causes the air to depart from the linearity called for by Charles' Law and the ideal gas law. In other words, we hypothesize that at atmospheric pressure, air stops behaving like an ideal gas above 40°C. We realize that this hypothesis runs counter to the tenets of the kinetic-molecular theory of gases, which indicate that at lower densities and higher temperatures, gas particles should behave more like the particles of an ideal gas, not less. It is possible that the failure of air to exhibit ideal gas behavior above 40°C is related to the fact that the composition of air is over 99% diatomic molecules (78.08% N_2 and 20.95% O_2). (2)

It appears to our team that the experimental setup itself is not the cause of the indicated departure from ideal gas behavior because the data follow the ideal gas prediction very closely up to approximately 40°C. Thus it would seem that the cause is some unknown factor particular to the behavior of air above 40°C.

Table 3. Predicted air volumes and percent differences.

Temperature, °C	Temperature, K	Predicted Volume, mL	Experimental Volume, mL	Percent Difference, %
−16.0	257.2	5.2	5.2	–
−6.9	266.3	5.38	5.4	0.37
0.1	273.3	5.52	5.6	1.45
15.2	288.4	5.82	5.8	0.34
20.3	293.5	5.92	6.0	1.35
26.8	300.0	6.06	6.2	2.31
44.0	317.2	6.41	6.7	4.30
50.0	323.2	6.53	7.1	8.73
57.2	330.4	6.67	7.5	12.4
60.1	333.3	6.73	7.7	14.4
67.8	341.0	6.89	8.5	23.3
71.0	344.2	6.95	9.0	29.5
75.0	348.2	7.03	9.6	36.6
75.8	349.0	7.05	9.8	39.0
76.9	350.1	7.07	10.0	41.4

Conclusion

This experiment provided an excellent demonstration of Charles' Law at temperatures below about 40°C. The linear variation of gas volume with temperature was clearly demonstrated from −16.0°C to 44.0°C. At temperatures above 40°C, air appears to depart from ideal gas behavior.

References

1. John D. Mays, *Chemistry for Accelerated Students* (Novare Science and Math, Austin, 2014).

2. *Marks' Standard Handbook for Mechanical Engineers* (McGraw Hill, NY, 1996).

Molecular Biology I Laboratory

Genetics of Organisms

Author:	Dana N. Allen
Team Member:	Ryan N. Adams
Date of Experiment:	October 23, 2014
Date Report Submitted:	October 28, 2014
Instructor:	Dr. Seagull
Class:	Molecular Biology I, B block

Abstract

Inheritance patterns rely heavily upon the basic principles of independent assortment and recombination during meiosis and the genetic makeup of chromosomes during fertilization. Mendelian genetics has provided a level of predictability for the expression of certain traits in offspring. However, inheritance patterns are often more complex than what can be calculated by simple Mendelian genetics, due to the fact that more than one gene often contributes to a single phenotype. Replicating the genetic methods laid out by Mendel and following scientists such as Thomas Hunt Morgan, we investigated the inheritance pattern of two genes and determined whether the two genes are autosomal or sex-linked using a multi-generation experiment in fruit flies, *Drosophila melanogaster*. A series of genetic crosses performed on flies that had either dominant (red) eyes or the recessive white eyes resulted in only males expressing the recessive white-eyed trait, and a cross of these progeny produced males expressing the recessive trait once again, confirming eye color to be a sex-linked trait. The genetic cross performed between flies with long wings and short wings yielded a majority of progeny with intermediate wings. A cross of a male and female, both with intermediate wings, produced progeny with a ratio of 1 : 2 : 1 of short wings : intermediate wings : long wings. This type of genotypic and phenotypic ratio confirms that the gene expression for a heterozygote exhibits incomplete dominance. We also determined that the gene for wing length was located on an autosomal chromosome since there was no difference in expression patterns between males and females.

Purpose

The purpose of this experment was to determine if a specific set of traits in the *Drosophila melanogaster* are dominant or recessive and whether they are sex-linked or autosomal chromosome traits.

Background

Gregor Mendel laid the groundwork for the study of inheritance, or genetics as we know it today. His work in pea plants can easily be translated to organisms that contain a simple genome such as *Drosophila melanogaster, Arabidopsis,* and *Canorhabditis elegans. Drosophila melanogaster*, the fruit fly, is one of the most common organisms used for genetic research. The relatively low maintenance, such as food requirements and space occupation, and the fact that one life cycle is completed in about twelve hours at room temperature and produces many offspring make it a very attractive species to study.

Mendel's studies allowed us to determine if a gene has a dominant or recessive characteristic and predict the genotype of a species based upon its phenotype. We expected individuals expressing a dominant phenotype, such as gray body, to have a greater number of offspring exhibiting the dominant phenotype if a monohybrid cross was performed with the recessive gray body. If a homozygous dominant fruit fly for gray body (GG) was crossed with a black body fruit fly (gg), then we expected the F_1 offspring to have a gray body with the genotype (Gg - heterozygote). If we crossed males and females from the F_1 generation, then we expected to see a phenotype of 3 : 1 (gray : black) and a genotype of 1 : 2 : 1 (homozygous dominant : heterozygote : homozygous recessive). Additionally, genotype and phenotype of offspring can be used to determine if a trait is sex-linked. If a gene is sex-linked, then males will most likely express the trait since sex-linked traits are carried on the X chromosome. Females rarely express the recessive trait unless both X chromosomes inherit the recessive trait. Sex-linked traits will not follow the inheritance patterns for autosomal chromosomes described above.

In this experiment, our team sought to determine the dominant eye color in *Drosophila melanogaster* and determine whether this trait is located on an autosomal chromosome or sex-linked. We also sought to determine the same characteristics for wing shape.

Experimental Procedure

The following equipment was used in this experiment:

vial containing *Drosophila melanogaster*
vials for mating flies (containing food)
glass bowl (10 cm × 4 cm) containing ice
ice in an ice bucket
camel-hair paintbrush (to manipulate immobilized flies)
dissecting microscope
petri dish
#1 Whatman filter paper (to soak up condensation and to keep the flies dry)
fly morgue (funnel and bottle containing baby oil)

Our team familiarized ourselves with proper techniques for characterizing the sex, traits, and immobilization of *Drosophila melanogaster* before beginning our experiment. Immobilization of fruit flies is dependent on temperature. The vial containing the flies was placed at an angle and twirled in an ice bucket for several minutes until the flies were no longer moving. Once immobilized, they were transferred to a petri dish containing the #1 Whatman filter paper. The petri dish was placed on ice when not being viewed under the dissecting microscope. The dissecting microscope was used to view the flies and determine sex and different traits. Once the flies were no longer required for experiments, they were placed in the fly morgue.

Our team was given 6 vials of flies, each vial containing flies with a different trait. The traits were as follows: red eyes, white eyes, brown eyes, long wings, short wings, and intermediate wings. Our team was most interested in studying the following traits: red and white eyes, and long and short wings.

Week 1
Once the flies were immobilized and sexed, we set up the following crosses in labeled vials. Three mating pairs were placed in each vial. These crosses were created in order to create a "true breeding" species, offspring that resemble the same phenotype as the parents and will also have a homozygous genotype for their trait. The crosses were as follows:

Eye color	1) Red × Red	Wing shape	3) Long × Long
	2) White × White		4) Short × Short

The mating vials were placed in a safe place and allowed to cross at room temperature. In one week, the F_1 generation was ready for observation.

Week 2
Vials 1–4 were immobilized and the offspring of the F_1 generation were enumerated, sexed, and specific trait characteristics were recorded. Our team was convinced that we had successfully created a homozygous expressing population. Therefore, we continued to the next cross. The crosses were set up in the labeled vials as described below. Once again, three mating pairs were placed in each vial. The crosses were as follows:

Eye color	5) Red × Red	Wing shape	9) Long × Long
	6) Red × White		10) Long × Short
	7) White × Red		11) Short × Long
	8) White × White		12) Short × Short

The mating vials were placed in a safe place and allowed to cross at room temperature. The F_2 generation was ready for observation within one week.

Week 3
Vials 5–12 were immobilized and the offspring of the F_2 generation were enumerated, sexed, and specific trait characteristics were recorded. Vials 6, 7, 10, and 11 gave interesting results that needed further characterization by crossing the progeny of the F_2 generation. Our team set up 4 additional vials (13–16) in order to perform these crosses and obtain data for the F_3 generation.

Results

Generation data are shown in Tables 1-3.

Table 1. F_1 generation data.

Vial #	Phenotype cross	Females	Males
1	Red eye × Red eye	73:red	75:red
2	White eye × White eye	68:white	72:white
3	Long wing × Long wing	63:long	73:long
4	Short wing × Short wing	72:long	65:long

Table 2. F_2 generation data.

Vial #	Phenotype cross	Females	Males
5	Red eye × Red eye	71:red	67:red
6	Red eye × White eye	65:red	70:red
7	White eye × Red eye	73:red	65:white
8	White eye × White eye	75:white	64:white
9	Long wing × Long wing	69:long	74:long
10	Long wing × Short wing	63:intermediate	70:intermediate
11	Short wing × Long wing	68:intermediate	76:intermediate
12	Short wing × Short wing	75:short	66:short

Table 3. F_3 generation data.

Vial #	Phenotype cross	Females	Males
13	Red eye × Red eye (progeny of vial #6)	63:red	31:red 35:white
14	Red eye × White eye (progeny of vial #7)	28:red 33:white	33:red 37:white
15	Intermediate wing × Intermediate wing (progeny of vial #10)	17:long 37:intermediate 12:short	12:long 29:intermediate 18:short
16	Intermediate wing × Intermediate wing (progeny of vial #11)	19:long 32:intermediate 13:short	15:long 35:intermediate 11:short

Discussion

The purpose of this experiment was to determine if a specific set of traits in the *Drosophila melanogaster* are dominant or recessive and whether they are sex-linked or autosomal chromosome traits. Our team studied two types of genes in two separate genetic crosses: the gene for eye color and the gene for wing shape.

We began by confirming the traits of the parentals we were supplied with regarding eye color and wing shape. As indicated in Table 1, the progeny proved to be identical to the parents. Therefore, we proceeded with the genetic crosses to determine which traits were dominant and whether the genes are located on sex chromosomes or autosomal chromosomes. According to pea plant genetic studies performed by Mendel, dominant traits should be the visible phenotype observed on all progeny if a homozygous parent crosses with a homozygous recessive organism. All the progeny will have a heterozygous phenotype for the trait in question. Additionally, sex-linked characteristics were characterized by the *Drosophila melanogaster* studies performed by Thomas Morgan. His laboratory discovered that some recessive traits were exhibited on males and not on female flies. It was possible for a female to carry one copy of the dominant trait on one X chromosome and the recessive trait on the other X chromosome, yet not express the recessive phenotype due to the dominance of the other. However, males only have one X chromosome (XY), and thus have one copy of each allele, which can be either dominant or recessive.

Table 2 describes the number of each progeny expressing a specific phenotype resulting from each cross. Our team made sure to have all the different types of crosses that can occur to ensure the best data analysis.

Eye Color
As expected, the crosses performed in vials 5 and 8 produced progeny that resembled the parents due to the homozygous genotype of each of the parents. However, vials 6 and 7 produced interesting results. A cross between homozygous red-eyed females and white-eyed males (vial 6) produced progeny with all red eyes. This genetic cross showed that red eyes are the dominant trait in flies with an equal number of males and females exhibiting this phenotype. More information was gathered from the genetic cross in vial 7. The cross between white-eyed females and red-eyed males produced progeny with the recessive, white-eyed trait in males only, and all females had the dominant, red-eye trait. These results are characteristic of a sex-linked trait, therefore we concluded that the gene for eye color is located on the X sex chromosome.

Wing Shape
Once again, as expected, the crosses performed in vials 9 and 12 produced progeny that resembled the parents. We obtained results that were not expected for the genetic crosses in vials 10 and 11. If one trait were dominant over the other, we would expect all progeny to express the dominant phenotype. However, all the progeny for vials 10 and 11 produced flies with intermediate wing length. This type of phenotype is consistent for a type of dominance known as incomplete dominance, where one trait is not dominant over the other and both traits "share" dominance. These results were also indicative of autosomal gene inheritance because expression was seen equally in both sexes.

Once the phenotypic results were obtained, genotypic analysis was completed in the Punnet square data represented in Figure 1.

Figure 1. F_2 Punnet square data for vials 6, 7, 10, and 11.

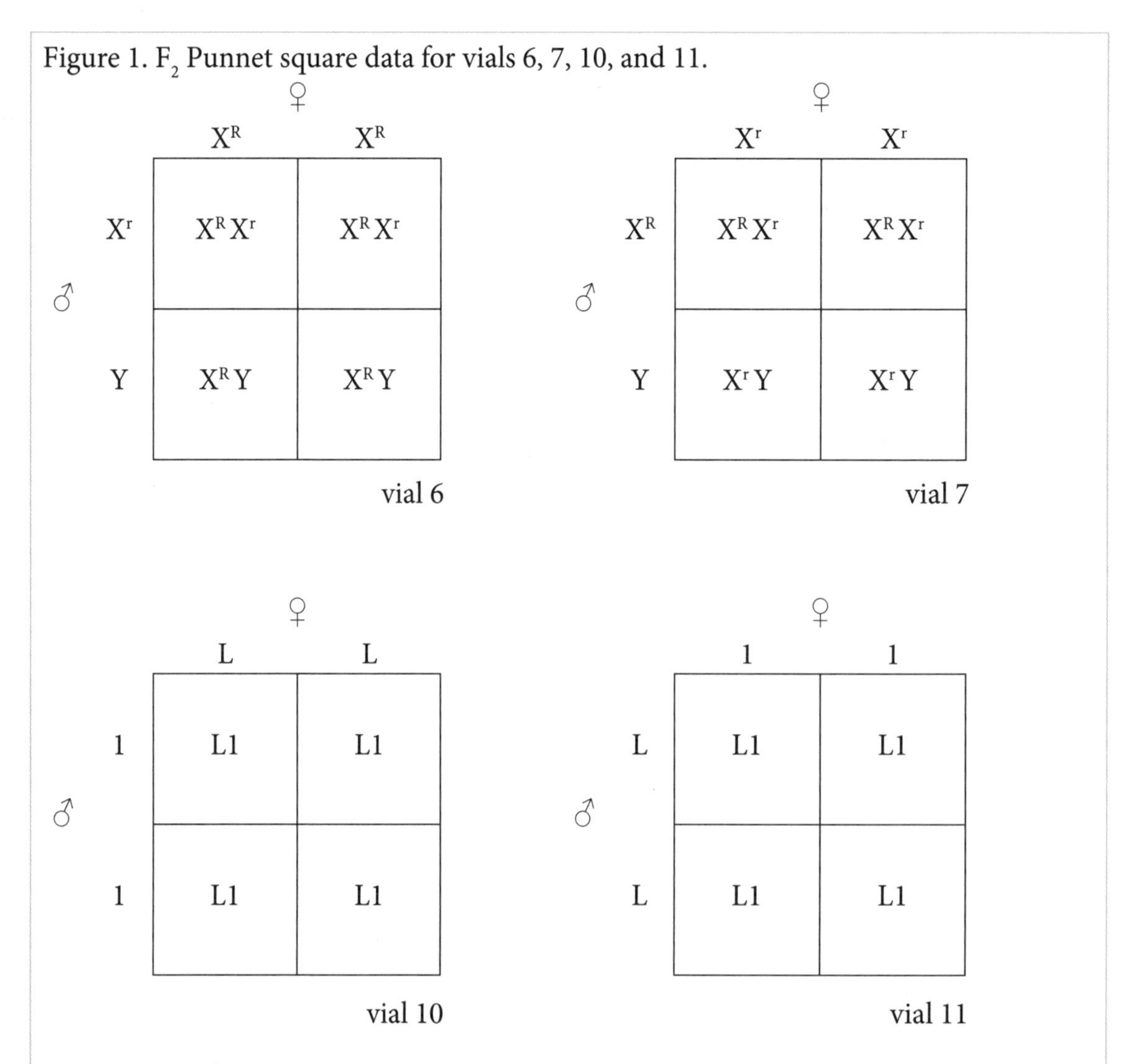

In a fashion similar to Mendel's work, we performed a genetic cross between males and females in the F_2 generation to create an F_3 generation. Table 3 represents the number of flies expressing a specific phenotype for the crosses in vials 13–16.

Eye Color
The crosses performed between a heterozygous red-eyed female and a red-eyed male produced a majority of the progeny expressing the dominant phenotype of red eyes. However, the recessive trait was expressed only in males. Once again, these data are characteristic of a sex-linked trait and confirm that the red eye trait is dominant.

Wing Shape
Mendelian genetic inheritance patterns for incomplete dominance suggest that when two species exhibiting incomplete dominance are crossed, a phenotypic and genotypic ratio of 1 : 2 : 1 (homozygous dominant : heterozygous intermediate : homozygous recessive) are observed. Indeed, upon examination of the crosses performed in vials 15 and 16, both proved to coincide with the expected results, confirming that neither

allele for wing shape has dominance over the other, and that this gene is located on an autosomal chromosome.

Once the phenotypic results were obtained, genotypic analysis was completed in the Punnet square data represented in Figure 2.

Figure 2. F_3 Punnet square data for vials 13–16.

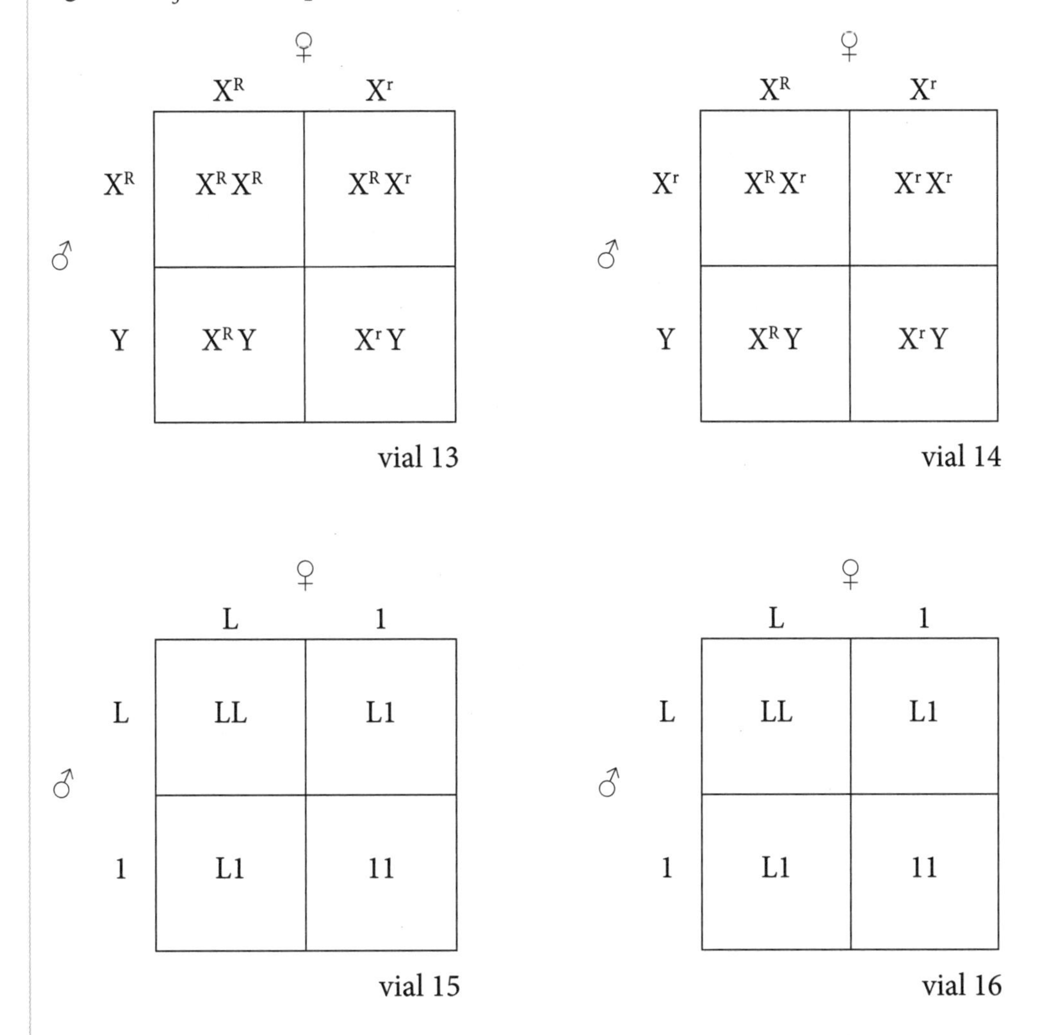

Conclusion

In conclusion, our experiment was very successful and we observed interesting results pertaining to specific genes in *Drosophila melanogaster*. We conclude that the allele for red eye color is dominant over the white eye color allele, and that the gene for eye color is located on the X chromosome. We determined that there is an incomplete dominance pattern observed for the gene responsible for wing length. Additionally, the gene for wing length is located on an autosomal chromosome. It was intriguing to repeat experiments that have been performed by Mendel and Morgan and to observe the classical inheritance patterns they characterized with their experiments.

Index